Active Learning Spaces and Technology

Advances in Higher and Further Education

Edited by Duncan Peberdy

First published in the United Kingdom in 2014 by

DroitwichNet
10 Mosel Drive
Droitwich Spa
Worcestershire
WR9 8DB

ISBN 978-0-9927903-0-1

Typeset by Duncan Peberdy

Printed and bound in the United Kingdom by Vernon Print and Design, Droitwich Spa

Contents

PART 8 - Acknowledgements

Contributors

Nicholas Burwell
Burwell Deakins Architects

Professor Charles Crook
Academic Director, Learning Sciences Research Institute, University of Nottingham

Roland Dreesden
Managing Director, Reflex Ltd

Sheila Egan
Business Development Manager, Snelling Business Systems

Nick Fitzpatrick
Director of AV, Universal AV

Andrew Milne, Ph.D.
CEO Tidebreak, Inc.

James Pearson-Jenkins
Senior Lecturer, Adult Acute Nursing and Academic Translation, University of Wolverhampton

Duncan Peberdy
Learning Spaces Specialist, Dalen Ltd (Manufactures of the TOP-TEC brand)

Caroline Pepper
Learning Spaces and Administration Manager, Loughborough University

Cathy Rex
Director of Library Services, University of the West of England

Sam Williams
Space Planning and Strategy Manager, University of Lincoln

Toby Wise
Managing Director, Snelling Business Systems

Robert Peberdy - COPY EDITOR

Neil Duffy - GRAPHIC DESIGN

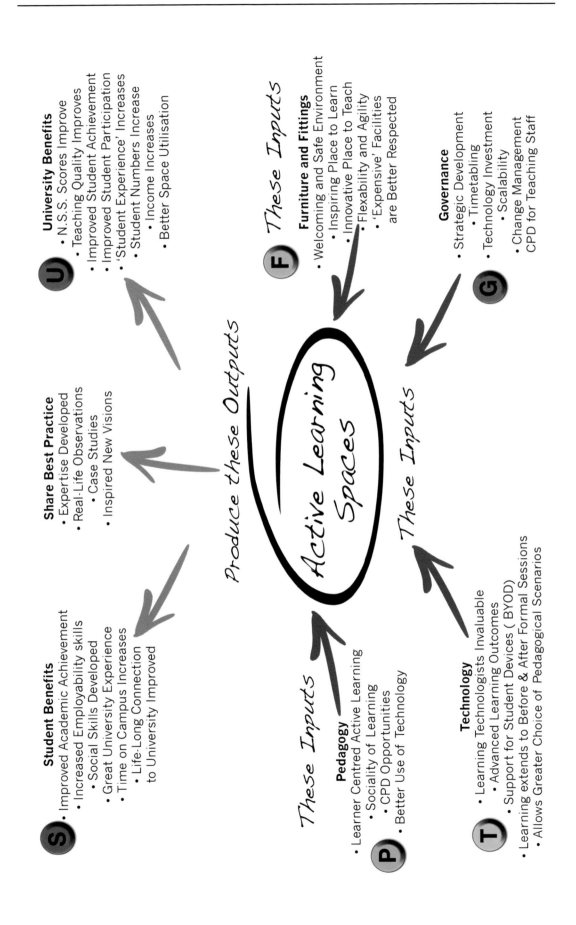

University Benefits
- N.S.S. Scores Improve
- Teaching Quality Improves
- Improved Student Achievement
- Improved Student Participation
- 'Student Experience' Increases
- Student Numbers Increase
- Income Increases
- Better Space Utilisation

U

Furniture and Fittings
- Welcoming and Safe Environment
- Inspiring Place to Learn
- Innovative Place to Teach
- Flexability and Agility
- 'Expensive' Facilities are Better Respected

F

These Inputs

Governance
- Strategic Development
- Timetabling
- Technology Investment
- Scalability
- Change Management CPD for Teaching Staff

G

Share Best Practice
- Expertise Developed
- Real-Life Observations
- Case Studies
- Inspired New Visions

Produce these Outputs

Active Learning Spaces

These Inputs

Student Benefits
- Improved Academic Achievement
- Increased Employability skills
- Social Skills Developed
- Great University Experience
- Time on Campus Increases
- Life-Long Connection to University Improved

S

These Inputs

Pedagogy
- Learner Centred Active Learning
- Sociality of Learning
- CPD Opportunities
- Better Use of Technology

P

Technology
- Learning Technologists Invaluable
- Advanced Learning Outcomes
- Support for Student Devices (BYOD)
- Learning extends to Before & After Formal Sessions
- Allows Greater Choice of Pedagogical Scenarios

T

Introduction

Personal experience in the promotion of audio visual equipment and technical furniture solutions has resulted in contact with consultants and integrators who are involved in creating learning spaces in universities. Over the years I have witnessed many clashes between academics and technology specialists. For example, a university that had a project designated as a Centre for Excellence in Teaching and Learning (CETL), sought to install ground-breaking visual collaboration equipment costing almost £100k. Two systems were to be installed, one in each of two campuses, but because the systems were purchased by academics without full input from IT or AV services, the necessary connectivity and support to make them work together to their potential was not forthcoming. Despite many meetings, connectivity issues were only resolved six months after installation, and curiously 24 hours before the university's vice chancellor officially opened the facility in the presence of an invited audience. Within a few days, the connectivity between the campuses was disconnected, and the systems worked independently. Whilst they still had some very positive effects, substantial advantages were lost. The equipment manufacturer was also responsible for some deficiencies.

Such ineptitude does a great disservice to students. In 2010, 43 per cent of UK school leavers started undergraduate programmes in 2010. This means that the breadth of academic ability across the student population is far greater than ever before. Universities now need to cater for less able students. Moreover, students are now required to pay high tuition fees. They therefore expect good facilities and standards of teaching.

It has long been argued by some educators that lectures are ineffective for students with a wide range of academic ability. Some years ago, Professor Robert Beichner from North Carolina State University in the USA sought to tackle the matter. He started a campaign for active learning spaces - SCALE-UP (Student Centred Active Learning Environments with Upside-down Pedagogy) - even though technology was relatively unsophisticated. A meeting with Professor Beichner at Portsmouth Business School in June 2013 led me to write an essay, The Case for Active Learning Environments in University Education. (Included here, in modified form, as Chapter 1) Through electronic distribution it quickly reached a large audience, particularly at universities. This in turn stimulated the preparation of this larger work. Active Learning Spaces and Technology seeks to take a holistic view of all the factors involved in creating effective environments for active learning, and to represent the experiences and concerns of the diverse specialists involved in creating such environments.

Duncan Peberdy

PART 1
A New Frontier in Learning

Chapter 1

Active Learning Environments in University Education
Duncan Peberdy

Lecture Theatres Aren't Working

Traditional lecture theatres were designed to enable large numbers of high-calibre students to hear expositions of knowledge and understanding. Students commonly listen to texts being read verbatim, without visual reinforcement or interaction. But lectures fail to cater for the wider range of students who are now entering universities because they treat all students as if they are equal, fail to ensure that knowledge is retained, and insufficiently engage students, resulting in poor attendance and feedback. Tiered lecture theatres are also inefficient because they cannot be used for other purposes. Now that many UK students are required to pay large fees, universities must pay greater attention to student expectations.

In the USA, over 200 universities and colleges have adopted active learning initiatives which have delivered dramatic improvements in every aspect of learning. New learning environments enable large student groups to work collaboratively in small teams in a single space, using visual information and creating knowledge as they learn from each other and their instructors. Students can jointly edit each other's work when displayed on team screens, or share material with a whole class via class screens arrayed around the room, or on team screens integrated into each table.

An excellent, pioneering example of active learning is the 'SCALE-UP' programme developed by Professor Bob Beichner at North Carolina State University, which was initially designed for teaching physics on introductory college courses. It features a collaborative, 'hands-on', computer-rich environment. Instead of passively listening to lecturers, students are set tasks that actively engage them in finding solutions through discussion and team work. They use high-quality audio visual facilities and online resources. All students are required to participate. The approach results in deeper learning and an enhanced undergraduate experience.

Research into the SCALE-UP outcomes over many years found that it improves problem-solving and conceptual understanding. It also generates more positive attitudes, and failure rates are drastically reduced, especially for women and members of minority groups. 'At risk' students do better.[1]

SCALE-UP now stands for Student Centred Active Learning Environment with Upside-down Pedagogies. Other acronyms or abbreviations have been coined for similar pedagogies for increasing student engagement and outcomes.

TEAL at MIT (Massachusetts Institute of Technology) = Technology Enhanced Active Learning

TBL at the University of Bradford = Team Based Learning

TILE at the University of Iowa = Transform, Interact, Learn, Engage

The 'Upside-down' element refers to the arrangement whereby information that would previously have been delivered as a lecture is provided in pre-session course work which students complete before team-based learning takes place.   This is also known as the 'flipped classroom' or 'reverse instruction' model of teaching, as advocated by Beichner and others including Salman Khan (Khan Academy), Jonathan Bergmann (Flippedlearning.com), and Aaron Sams (Sams Learning Designs).

There is no best way to teach a class, but some instructional methods have been shown through research to enhance learning gains by students, especially at the deeper levels of Bloom's Taxonomy.[2] Instructional strategies such as collaborative learning,[3] problem-based learning,[4] and team-based learning,[5] depend upon successful interactions between students working together in a supportive community. Traditional classrooms do not facilitate such student interaction, and whilst instruction in traditional lecture theatres can be improved by adopting such methods,[6] the improvement occurs in spite of the environment. Active learning classroom environments remove some of the barriers that prevent instructors from implementing pedagogical innovations.[7]

Academic Benefits

Students learn more in active learning rooms, forming closer relationships with their peers and instructors.   A single room can be used for a short 'lecture' to set the scene and group learning. It has been observed that 'Students enjoy the classroom experience and they are fully engaged with the learning process.'[8]   Failure rates are reduced, and the academic results of the best students are increased.   There is no 'back of the class' in which students can hide, and team projects generate beneficial peer pressure. Whilst technology enables group interactions, the key dynamics are those of students becoming tutors and instructors becoming coaches. A consistent message from studies of is that its dedicated spaces and associated methods provide a much more enjoyable and challenging learning experience for students. The benefits of increased attendance, engagement and attainment have been replicated at universities and colleges across the USA, Australia and Asia.[9]

Tables and Teams

The most obvious outward features of active learning are student-centred tables and technology. Technology in this case means anything that is used to facilitate visual learning: displays, whiteboards, projectors and microphones (so all students can hear and be heard). In most American active learning environments, nine students typically sit in groups of three at round tables that are 7ft (2.1m) in diameter. The diameter is not accidental; studies revealed that smaller tables made the students feel cramped, while larger tables prevented table-wide discussions.[10] Three-person groups are also preferred on the basis of research, [11] although other sizes could be facilitated. Each group of three students shares a laptop computer, but the 'group' display is located away from the table either fixed to a wall or on a mobile mount.

With nine students on each table working as three teams, each team is likely to interfere with the work of the others. Research has also shown that collaboration declines when a team numbers more than six, because larger groups enable some members to avoid contributing. Nine students on one table may have a similar effect, especially when all groups are working simultaneously on the same material.

The UK Experience

UK universities began to introduce active learning environments about 16 years after SCALE-UP was launched at North Carolina State University. Different seating arrangements were preferred, usually a table that accommodated one team of five or six students. Such tables are more efficient that American round tables. More students can be accommodated within a given area, and each table can have a dedicated integrated display. Teams of six or fewer work better collaboratively than nine. Even where educators want to follow the methodology of having nine students on a table, large plectrum-shaped tables that integrate the display are being used. At the University of Bradford, a team based learning room was installed in the faculty of Life Sciences during summer 2012, specifically for pharmacy. It accommodates 108 students at 18 tables (6 per table).

To be successful, instruction in an active learning environment must emphasise the students' learning rather than an instructor's lecturing. Therefore, there is no 'front' to the classroom, and ample space is provided for teaching staff to circulate amongst the students asking questions and giving support. The TBL room at the University of Bradford[12] has proved incredibly successful. When first-year undergraduates were faced with conducting their second-year studies in traditional rooms and lecture theatres, they argued for the provision of a second room. From the outset, Bradford also realised that their room's success would ultimately be reliant on its audio Visual and IT equipment as this would enable participation by every student.

A Catalyst for Change

"Change is a problem because it unsettles people, but sometimes unsettling
people gives them a fresh start."[13]

The benefits of active learning extend beyond the experience itself. Faced with competition from online education, social interaction is something that universities can claim to provide, and this is a central feature of active learning. It also provides many more benefits for universities:

- Active learning enhances the student experience through providing a supportive learning environment
- It raises academic achievements through encouraging a deeper understanding of subjects and concepts

- It develops transferable skills relevant to employment, such as problem- solving, critical thinking and capacity for teamwork
- It makes better use of space as rooms can be used more extensively than lecture theatres
- It reduces drop-out rates, thereby raising student completion rates and strengthening income

Instructor Training

A requirement for the introduction of active learning is that instructors must receive training before they are allowed to teach in these situations. It is vital for instructors to be effective with visual and audio tools to support active learning and student construction of knowledge. Ineffective use of active learning spaces compromises investment because it inhibits student attainment. Teachers should be obliged to attend a formal course of one or two days that emphasises the integration of new pedagogies with room facilities, including the challenges involved in preparing for active learning.

Active learning makes novel demands on teachers who have taught in lecture theatres. How do they convert existing lectures into new activities? How do they prepare students for active learning? How are successful groups created? How should students' progress be assessed? What should happen if things go wrong?

At the University of Iowa, existing and new instructors alike undertake a three-day TILE workshop (Transform, Interact, Learn, Engage) to prepare them for active learning methodologies. In institutions with only a few active learning environments, typically rooms are only bookable for use by instructors who have undergone the necessary training.

Risk Assessment

An institution that wishes to develop active learning will need to analyse costs and other factors. The kinds of questions that might be asked include the following.
Does this fit within the university's strategic aims in providing, better student experience, better academic outcomes, developing transferable skills, maintaining student income streams, and helping with space utilisation? Can the institution undertake organisational change? Can the necessary change in pedagogy be organised?

Economic Investment

Active learning environments are more expensive than spaces without technology, and the best technology for active learning, so-called 'invisible technology' is the most expensive. However, it has been found that installations with expensive technology and high-quality furniture, are treated with respect by students, and on-going maintenance and refurbishment costs are lower. Moreover, enhanced use of technology in specially equipped rooms can act as a catalyst for improving technology use in all teaching spaces. Students now arrive at university having experienced the use of interactive whiteboards in school classrooms and expect good facilities in return for their fees.

For universities, active learning rooms can be attractive assets in recruiting students.

The Latest 2013 Research Findings

Using 12 engagement factors (collaboration, focus, active involvement, opportunity to engage, repeated exposure to material through multiple means, in-class feedback, real-life scenarios, ability to engage ways of learning best, physical movement, stimulation, feeling comfortable to participate, and creation of an enriching experience), Dr Lennie Scott-Webber and her team researched the effect on formal learning sessions from the provision of three new environments featuring mobile chairs with an integrated work surface, small group collaborative tables, and small group collaborative tables with integrated displays; all developed through evidence-based research and products of Steelcase Inc.

Using an Active Learning Post-Occupancy Evaluation™ that was developed to synthesize student engagement from previous multiple research studies, the study evaluated 127 students and 17 faculty members at three institutions. Statistically significant improvements between the traditional row-by-column seating and the new active learning areas were recorded for all 12 student engagement factors, clearly demonstrating that there is a relationship between the impacts of a formal learning area on student engagement – and that correctly designed active learning areas increase this substantially.

This study - undertaken by researchers from Steelcase Education Solutions in 2013 – has positive implications for higher education policy makers and those responsible for advancing the quality of learning and teaching, to ensure that new educational spaces that connect intentional learning behaviours with pedagogical practices are guided by evidence-based design.

Dr Lennie's full report – **Built Environments Impact Behaviours: Results of an Active Learning Post-Occupancy Evaluation** – can be found at www.scup.org/phe.

References

1.   Beichner, R. J., Saul, J.M., Abbott, D.S., Morse, J., Deardorff, D., Allain, R.J., Bonham, S.W., Dancy, M., Risley, J. (2007). 'Student-Centered Activities for Large Enrollment Undergraduate Programs (SCALE-UP) Project', in Redish, E.F., Cooney, P.J. (eds.), Research-Based Reform of University Physics.

2.   Krathwohl, D.R. (2002). 'A revision of Bloom's Taxonomy: An overview'. Theory into Practice, vol 41, pp. 212-18.

3.   Johnson, D.W., Johnson, R.T., & Smith, K.A., (1991). Cooperative Learning: Increasing College Faculty Instructional Productivity.

4.   Savery, J., Duffy, T. (1995). 'Problem Based Learning: An Instructional Model and its Constructivist Framework', Educational Technology, vol. 35, pp 31-38.

5.   Michaelsen, L.K., Sweet, M., Parmelee, D.X. (eds) (2008). Team-Based Learning: Small Group Learning's Next Big Step (New Directions for Teaching and Learning series, No. 116).

6.   Mazur, E. (1997). Peer Instruction: A User's Manual.

7.   Gaffney, J.D.H., Richards, E., Kustusch, M.B., Ding, L., Beichner, R. (2008). 'Scaling up Educational Reform', Journal of College Science Teaching, vol. 37, pp. 48-53.

8.   Kamei, R.K., Cook, S., Puthucheary J., Starmer C.F. (2012). '21st Century Learning in Medicine: Traditional Teaching Versus Team-based Learning'. Medical Science

Educator, vol. 22, pp. 57-64.

9. Deslauriers, L., Schelew, E., Wieman, C. (2011). 'Improved Learning in a Large-Enrollment Physics Class'. Science , vol. 332, pp. 862-864.

10. Beichner, R.J., et al. (2007) (as ref. 1).

11. Heller, P, Hollabaugh, M. (1992). 'Teaching Problem Solving through Cooperative Grouping. Part 2: Designing Problems and Structuring Groups'. American Journal of Physics, vol. 60, pp.637-44.

12. 18 Synergy Tables (Teardrop design) manufactured by TOP-TEC (www.top-tec.co.uk) and integrated by Universal Audio Visual (www.uniav.com).

13. Sean O'Driscoll, Manager, Bristol City Football Club, June 2013.

Chapter 2

Technology in Education

Sheila Egan
Business Development Manager, Snelling Business Systems

In the twenty-first century technology has become a prevalent feature of ordinary life, including education. The integration of the internet into daily activities has changed the way in which people interact, as have mobile devices. Most people possess mobile phones. The choice not to have a mobile phone is viewed as unusual. These developments have had a significant impact on the way in which children view the world. It is now the norm of children to use mobile tablet devices, as has been highlighted by the design of a baby's bouncing chair with an integrated holder for a 'tablet'. However, there are negative elements to this, such as the sad growth of cyber bullying.

So what influence does the prevalence of mobile devices and other technology have on the way in which children and young people are taught? In UK primary education it is now expected that a classroom will feature interactive technology equipment, primarily interactive whiteboard technology (IWB). Teaching has evolved to work around the idea of learning in short bursts with a strong emphasis on interactive learning. An unwritten rule of thumb is that an activity should last for the child's age plus five minutes; thus entry-level primary children will be taught in nine-minute bursts, rising to sixteen minutes for final-year primary children. Whether this is as a result of shorter attention spans, or merely that teachers have evolved content to focus on interactive learning, is a moot matter. The digital age is here, and teachers and technology providers alike must work within it.

It is important that technology-providers in education understand that children today have grown up surrounded by technology and are much less fearful of it than their elders. They acquire an instinctive understanding of how to use and interact with the technologies provided for them. Even the headmaster of Eton College has declared with regard to technology that schools must "be open minded, learn to embrace it, use it" or risk becoming irrelevant and wither (Daily Mail, 7 Dec. 2013).

The MIT (Massachusetts Institute of Technology) project initiative 'TEAL' (Technology Enhanced Active Learning) focused on the gap between how students actually learn as opposed to the traditional 'passive learning' approach. It worked around the same principles that are used in primary education, such as learning in twenty-minute bursts followed by a different, related activity. The TEAL project took this further and developed the idea of social learning, through putting together groups of three students with varying levels of knowledge on a topic to stimulate peer-to-peer learning. The arrangement required a lecturer to be equipped with a wireless microphone to enable him or her to move around a room and interact with groups or with the class as a whole. Multiple projectors would enable content to be repeated or made available for each group. Thus technology became an integral tool to support the style of teaching rather than content being dictated by the technology available, or merely allowing passive learning with one person teaching many students.

The next step was to devise social collaborative learning whereby three to six students work in a group, around a screen, and groups interact, learning from each other in a large collaborative workspace. This means that Group One can work on an idea, then share their content with Group Six, and each group learns and adapts. This type of interactive learning can be overseen by a central facilitator, with periodic sessions of returning to a central focal point, thus ensuring that all ideas and content are noticed and shared. Ideally this generated content would be captured via traditional lecture capture equipment, and then made available to students via a VLE (Virtual Learning Environment). If the institution has multiple-purpose flat screens positioned throughout a building, available for use by students with mobile devices, group learning can continue after a class. Thus there will be not just socially collaborative workspaces but socially collaborative buildings and campuses. Just as online facilities such as Facebook enable people with similar interests to connect, learning can continue beyond the classroom via mobile devices and VLEs.

Content captured via lecture capture systems, in which most higher education institutes have invested in to some degree, has been shown to enhance student engagement rather than detract from it. Attendance is higher on courses that utilise lecture capture. There will be a spike in content re-accessed during revision before exams. Students may not re-watch an entire lecture but will find key topics for their revision.

In this brave new technologically advanced world, it is worth remembering that students generally express a wish to spend more time with lecturers or course tutors. So technology does not replace a desire for human relationships. Lecturers should not believe that the technology is employed to replace their teaching methods: it should enhance their existing skills and methods. It also allows students to continue their (digital) contact with teachers outside the classroom. Technology providers must ensure that technology works seamlessly and intuitively to break down any barriers, created either through fear or inertia, and that technology shows itself to enhance interaction. It is important for providers to listen to feedback from lecturers and make adaptions. Reliability is also a key factor in the adoption of new technologies: integrators must ensure that systems are reliable before they are used by academic staff. Those specifying systems to integrators can assist by providing clear requirements.

Integrators and system providers must advance with the digital age by obtaining feedback from users of technology and modifying their systems. It is also desirable that installed systems can be updated as required, because they cannot be replaced with every technological advance. The overall picture of higher education in the digital age is one of advancement in the adoption of technology alongside the continuance of human contact and interaction for advancement of knowledge as a central, guiding principle.

Chapter 3

Learning Space Design: Beyond Collaborative Learning

Charles Crook

Academic Director, Learning Sciences Research Institute, University of Nottingham

How is a learner's experience influenced by spatial design? In recent years this question has been considered by researchers and practitioners from a wide range of academic disciplines, notably psychology, human geography, anthropology, sociology, information science, and that special mix of folk who gather under the banner of 'technology enhanced learning' (or 'TEL'). This essay will identify four dimensions of 'learner experience' that have been addressed through initiatives of spatial design, but will focus on one of them, namely the management of multiple visual projections. This is a dimension of educational practice that has been neglected in learning space design; that is to say, relatively little attention has been paid to innovation concerned with the representation of learning material – at least as this might be managed within more expository formats of educational practice.

Four Dimensions of Learning that Inspire Space Design

The distinctions identified in this section are by not the only ones used for organising the field of concern (e.g., see Bligh and Crook, 2014) for some alternatives). Yet it is helpful that they relate to central themes in the psychology of learning, because they express four recurring psychological states, each of which may be modulated by aspects of spatial design. In sum, from the learning psychologist's perspective, research on space design has been variously addressing the following: the social, the affective, the instrumental, or the computational aspect of the learner's predicament.

Of these, the social theme has attracted the most interest for research and development. That interest has largely been about how the furnishings and topography of a learning space can be designed to influence the character, quality or frequency of certain interpersonal exchanges. What motivates this, of course, is the idea that such social encounters play a crucial part in stimulating the progress of learning. Spatial design has been identified as an orchestrating force for these exchanges. Designs that pursue this idea have been most visible through the re-casting of traditional spaces (such as libraries) into 'information commons' or 'learning commons'. In these community spaces, learners will find not just extra comfort in their personal space, but various configurations of furniture that invite productive interactions with their student peers. Moreover, this same imperative to socialise the learning space applies in virtual worlds of learning, as well as in physical ones (cf., Andreas et al. 2010).

The dominance of this social theme in the literature of learning spaces is not surprising – given contemporary emphasis within psychology on the significance of interpersonal connections for effective learning (e.g., Rogoff et al. 1996). But the design of space should not be driven by a single-minded preoccupation with collaboration, as if group work must be the inevitable configuration for all experiences of study. First of all, the sociality felt within learning spaces is not only to be found within the mutuality that is typical of collaborating (Crook, 2013). The actual appeal of a 'learning commons' resides also in other more nuanced senses of the 'social' and does not depend upon relentless collaborative study, at least in the form of task-focused group work (Crook and Mitchell. 2012). Secondly, although innovation in space design often does seem oriented towards stimulating collaborative learning, designers can be receptive to other themes in the experience of learning, although these have been less fully researched. These will be examined in turn.

The next consideration is the affective dimension of learning. Although the significance of emotions in learning has certainly been recognised and explored (e.g., Baker et al. 2013), little is known about how the aesthetic ambience of a learning space, or its creature comforts, influences engagement with learning. The care taken over décor in many learning commons suggests considerable faith in the proposition that such details make a difference. Yet how much difference, or what its form, is poorly understood. When pressed to reflect on the material conditions of new study spaces, students often dwell upon their functional adequacy and seem less moved by affect that might arise from comfort or décor (Cox, 2011; Crook and Mitchell, 2012).

A third theme directing design innovation concerns the instrumental dimension of learning. This is straightforward at one level: it is about ensuring that a learning environment is adequately resourced. Yet this can demand a variety of solutions and degrees of ingenuity - depending on the special needs of a discipline. Roth and Hsu (2013) have illustrated the subtle relationships that can exist between space and the provision of specialist equipment as it is organised for activity in science classrooms. So design innovation that addresses the instrumental dimension of learning tends to be crafted according to the needs of a discipline. Nevertheless, there are initiatives that endeavour to create more generic solutions – initiatives whereby the instrumental resources of a space stimulate reflection and invention. An example would be the 'Box', an area equipped for these purposes at the London School of Economics (Harrison, 2006).

The final dimension of learning that addresses design is the 'computational'. This is more cognitive than social or affective, and more reflective than instrumental. The term refers to situations where the design of an environment is implicated in the presentation of material that requires the learner to 'compute' understandings or solutions – a design to stimulate thought. The remainder of this chapter will explore one significant realisation of this species of design possibility. It is one that has failed to attract the consideration it deserves.

Multiple Projection: Spatially Managing Representations for Learning

As argued above, the design of learning spaces should not be understood as a venture that is exclusively about the social needs of educational practice, it is also about representational needs. This consideration will shift our focus away from collaboration as a theme, but it may also seem to shift the focus away from the learner: but it will become clear below that this is not entirely the case. For it is true that concern with representational needs relates more to the expository role of the teacher and associated cognitive (or computational) demands on the learner.

Much teaching exposition proceeds through an effort to integrate voice and image. The preferred tool for achieving this is the ubiquitous slideshow. The spaces required for this teaching format require little investment in design. The learner simply needs to be able to hear the presenter clearly and to see the visual presentation. However, the structure of the slideshow format is not without critics. Much has been written about the oppressive influence of PowerPoint (and its relatives) on expository teaching. However, the linear sequence of frames that typically characterises this mode of presentation is not the only way in which it may be managed. Frames may also be presented simultaneously as well as successively. At least, this becomes possible where the design of the teaching and learning space is adapted to support such multiple presentation. Unfortunately, this is a rare situation.

The case for simultaneous presentation of representations in learning needs to be made carefully. For instance, it might suggest that learners will be plunged into stressful demands of multi-tasking. Although multi-screen environments are becoming widespread for the domestic consumption of entertainment (Lin, 2013), the imposition of multiple screens in a demanding educational environment seems more controversial. Indeed, practices in which students' might be fractured have been criticised for dominating the learner's familiar (desktop) digital experience (Crook and Barrowcliff, 2001; Judd, 2013; Risko et al. 2013). Conventional media multi-tasking often has a pacey temporal structure which aims to create a sense of action and excitement. However, in the case of representations that are multi-projected in a teaching environment, a greater degree of intelligent scaffolding by the instructor should be expected. So the learner's experience here should be different.

Where multiple projection has been discussed (Bligh and Coyle, 2013; Bligh and Lorenz, 2010), its pedagogic rationale has generally centred on efforts to manage visual comparison and contrast. For instance, a lecturer in classical art history may find considerable advantage in being able to show multiple perspectives on a Roman statue, and do this simultaneously (cf. Bligh and Lorenz, 2010). In order to stress the value of this simultaneous comparison (and counteract concerns about unproductive multi-tasking), it is necessary to invoke some findings from the cognitive psychology of attention. An effect that is well established in that literature is termed 'change blindness'. Basically the effect concerns the failure of a human observer to notice small changes in a visual representation upon its successive presentation – even if the interval between these presentations is very short (Rensink et al, 1997). This defines a surprising limitation in human short-term visual memory. However, the limitation may be compensated for by the careful tutoring of attention in circumstances of simultaneous visual access. Therefore, the potential to orchestrate student attention in this way encourages designs for expository teaching that allow multiple or simultaneous presentation of visual materials.

But comparative study is not the only attentional structure that encourages designs for multiple projection. Another presentational structure would be a 'parent-and-offsprings' configuration, where one key projected frame serves as the anchor or reference point for a several offspring frames, these being 'horizontally' related to each other while 'vertically' related to the anchor. Yet another visual structure would be one in which the contrasts were systematically related, in the sense of illustrating a sequential process of some kind. An example in engineering might be the successive states of a two-stroke combustion engine. Here a learner might be encouraged to construct an understanding of the process by repeated scrutiny of the successive frames – a form of classroom inspection that is protected from the limitations of change blindness.

Experience suggests that there are actually three motives for providing spaces for multiple projection. One is representational, as sketched above; that is, the configuration creates novel opportunities for learners to 'compute' fresh understandings of visually represented material - in terms of the possibilities created for comparison and contrast, or the possibilities for constructing inter-relationships in some visual sequence. A second motive is more performative. This relates to the embodied nature of exposition: typically a teacher acts so as to integrate their gestures, movement, voice, etc. with the content of projected representations during an exposition. In the classic slideshow, the images move (in linear sequence) and the speaker (typically) stays still. In a situation of multiple projection, it is more the images that stay still and the speaker moves, perhaps shifting stance and gesture between the display surfaces. At least, that is a potential that is built into multiple-projection arrangements. In short, the spatial distribution of visual representations invites a more animated, more expressive physical relationship with their presence. Finally, a third motive for this design invokes again the theme of sociality in learning. Although multiple projection has been discussed in the context of typical teacher exposition, the technologies of multiple projection can also support small group participation, at least when the personal devices of learners are programmed to interact with aspects of the shared screen display (Bligh and Sharples, 2010).

Conclusions

How are learners served when people purposively influence the design of learning spaces? It has been suggested here that spatial solutions have typically related to one or more of four psychological themes inherent within learning relationships: themes concerning the social, affective, instrumental and computational or cognitive dimensions of learning. It is the social that has historically been most vigorously addressed. Much of our concern with the design of learning spaces has apparently been driven by the goal of orchestrating creative and productive opportunities for learners to relate to each other or to their tutors. This is a proper concern and one that has generated a rich variety of design solutions. But it is not the only way in which we can consider the affordances (possibilities) of spatial design. The preceding section has sought to give focus to a neglected psychological theme, namely designs for environments that support the display of multiple simultaneous representations. With the advent of new and relatively inexpensive projection technologies, interest in the potential for this design challenge should expand in all sectors of education in the near future.

References

Andreas, K., Tsiatsos, T., Terzidou, T., Pomportsis, A. (2010). Fostering Collaborative Learning in Second Life: Metaphors and Affordances, Computers and Education, vol. 55, pp. 603-15

Baker, M., Andriessen, J. and Järvelä, S. (2013). Affective Learning Together: Social and Emotional Dimensions of Collaborative Learning. (New Perspectives on Learning and Instruction series).

Bligh, B., Lorenz, K. (2010) 'Vorsprung durch Technik: Multi-display Learning Spaces and Art-historical Method', in: Bentkowska, A., Pilcher, J., (eds.) Technology and 'the Death of Art History'.

Bligh, B., Coyle, D. (2013). 'Re-mediating Classroom Activity with a Non-linear, Multi-display Presentation Tool. Computers and Education, vol. 63, pp. 337-57.

Bligh, B., Sharples, M. (2010). 'The Affordances of Presentations in Multi-display Learning Spaces for Supporting Small Group Discussion', in Sustaining TEL: From Innovation to Learning and Practice. Proceedings of 5th European Conference on Technology Enhanced Learning.

Bligh, B., Crook, C. (2014). 'Learning Spaces: Departure Points for a Spatial Turn in Technology Enhanced Learning, in Duval, E., Sharples, M., Sutherland, R., (eds.), A Reader in Technology-enhanced Learning.

Cox, A.M. (2011). 'Students' Experience of University Space: An Exploratory Study'. International Journal of Teaching and Learning in Higher Education, vol. 23, pp. 197-207.

Crook, C.K. (2013). 'Varieties of "togetherness" in Learning - and their Mediation'. In Baker, M., Andriessen, J., Järvelä, S. (eds.), Affective Learning Together: Social and Emotional Dimensions of Collaborative Learning (New Perspectives on Learning and Instruction series).

Crook, C.K., Barrowcliff, D. (2001). 'Ubiquitous Computing on Campus: Patterns of Engagement by University Students'. International Journal of Human-Computer Interaction. Vol. 13, pp. 245-58.

Crook, C.K., Mitchell, G. (2012). Ambience in Social Learning: Student Engagement with New Designs for Learning Spaces Cambridge Journal of Education. Vol. 42, pp. 121-39.

Harrison, A. (2006). London School of Economics. BOX in Oblinger D.G. (ed.), Learning Spaces (EDUCAUSE eBook, chap. 23. available at http://net.educause.edu/ir/library/pdf/PUB7102.pdf).

Judd, T. (2013). 'Making Sense of Multitasking: Key Behaviours', Computers and Education, vol. 63, pp. 358-67

Lin, T.T.C. (2013). 'Convergence and Regulation of Multi-screen Television: The Singapore Experience', Telecommunications Policy, vol. 37, pp. 673-85.

Rensink, R.A., O'Regan, J.K., Clark, J.J. (1997). 'To See or Not to See: The Need for Attention to Perceive Changes in Scenes', Psychological Science vol. 8, pp. 368-73.

Risko, E.F., Buchanan, D., Medimorec, S., Kingstone, A. (2013). Everyday Attention: Mind Wandering and Computer Use during Lectures, Computers and Education, vol. 68, pp. 275-83.

Rogoff, B., Matusov, E., White, C. (1996). 'Models of Learning in a Community of Learners', in Olson, D.R., Torrance, N. (eds.), Handbook of Education and Human Development: New Models of Learning, Teaching, and Schooling.

Roth, W.M., Hsu, P.L. (2013). 'Space, Relations, and the Learning of Science'. Cultural Studies of Science Education, vol. 8 (published online).

Chapter 4

Simultaneously Viewing Multiple PowerPoint Slides

Duncan Peberdy

In the previous chapter, the benefit to student understanding of complex information and visual images that are best compared and contrasted together is outlined. Rather than determining how to achieve this starting with a blank canvas, Multi-Slides software provides Microsoft PowerPoint with the functionality to deliver engaging environments, making immediate use of the many teaching rooms that are already equipped with dual projection, and for little additional cost. The original basis for dual projection was so that, for example, information on a PowerPoint slide can be compared and reinforced with a different source of information. Visualisers are especially good in this respect.

As Microsoft PowerPoint is available in every teaching space, how much better would information be understood if instead of two separate sources of information being shown, two consecutive PowerPoint slides are viewed? Why stop there? Projectors and displays are now a small fraction of the cost of the time when two units were first routinely installed. In fact, one room at the University of Nottingham has six projectors that display consecutive slides around the room, all from a single computer with PowerPoint.

How Can Multiple PowerPoint Slides be Viewed Simultaneously?

Most computers have a single graphics card that sends the image to a single display. Graphics cards that can provide images to 2 or 4 displays are inexpensive and readily available. A computer needs one of these cards and each projector has to have a display cable back to the same computer. Finally, a computer needs to have the Multi-Slides software application installed to provide PowerPoint with this engaging facility.

The software is simple to use; each time you start a new slideshow you choose how many slides you want to see simultaneously and continue. This can be programmed as a default, and of course you can still just choose to see one slide at a time.

When students have information arranged in a way that provides reinforcement of complex subjects, or, as in the case of Classics or Art History, multiple images so comparisons can be made, learning advances. This can be from both the better understanding and peer discussions that it sparks.

If an interactive device is available, then annotations can be made to slides, which are retained at the end of the slideshow. When additional explanations are required, or feedback from students is recorded, instead of writing these on a flip chart or dry-erase board, Multi-Slides inserts a blank slide on demand, enabling these valuable real-time editions to be digitally captured as an additional PowerPoint slide - in context with the original material - which is uploaded to the VLE.

There are yet more benefits to learning that having multiple PowerPoint slides on view delivers:

- Slides are on view for longer, so information can be better assimilated or considered
- 'Speaker Notes' can be relayed to a lectern display for only the lecturer to see
- Slideshows can still be authored on any computer

For an existing room that already has two or more displays, it is unlikely that they are both connected to a single PC. For the AV team there is some rewiring work to undertake, and a new graphics card to purchase and install, but these are both insignificant investments compared to the student benefits that follow.

More information on Multi-Slides can be found at www.multi-slides.com

The image opposite shows an example of a 3-display Multi-Slides installation.
In this example, three consecutive slides are shown. In a different configuration, Multi-Slides can show consecutive slides on screens 1 and 3, with screen 2 showing a different source of information; a Excel spreadsheet, a live website, an image from a WolfVision visualiser.
Or, screen 3 can show the supporting information, with PowerPoint on screens 1 and 2.
These and other configurations are simple to choose.

Chapter 5

Full-Participation Learning Spaces for the Twenty-first Century

Andrew J. Milne, Ph.D.
CEO Tidebreak, Inc.

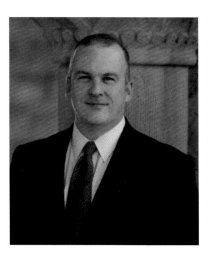

The best technology-enhanced learning spaces aim to provide exceptional experiences for students and teaching staff. The term 'exceptional experience' means much more than merely a high-quality audio visual presentation. Truly exceptional experiences are ones that draw individuals into a dynamic technology-augmented discussion of topics and exchange of ideas that ultimately results in positive learning outcomes. What are the basic considerations for providing exceptional experiences? The design considerations draw largely on understandings about the way in which groups work with information in the 'interaction Age'.[1]

Tidebreak, a Silicon Valley company with origins at Stanford University, has been developing next-generation tools for full-participation learning. The team at Tidebreak draws insight from research findings in fields related to design thinking, human-computer interaction and computer-supported collaborative work to deliver exceptional experiences.

Moving to a Learner-Centered Approach

Tidebreak subscribes to a definition of teaching as the purposeful structuring of experiences from which students cannot escape without learning. Such an outlook is fundamental to the pedagogical approaches alternately labeled 'active learning', 'collaborative learning', and 'problem-based learning', among others. In experiences designed for group contexts, interpersonal interactions need to be accommodated alongside interaction with material because social processes related to content development play a significant role in collaborative work. (In one study, the amount of activity focused on navigating the social process of the group – compared with handling information directly - was approximately 40 per cent.[2]) Thus it is important not only to consider how technology can support information access, one must also consider how it can support and/or not interfere with the natural flow of team dynamics.

Many classroom systems focus on how to support an instructor (or student) as they are presenting information to a class. This emphasis on transmitting content follows from traditional, teaching-centric thinking. Learner-centric pedagogies, in contrast, challenge us to think more about how to help all students become more actively engaged with material through their learning experiences. Rather than confining students to a passive experience, we need to consider how to engage students more extensively in learning activities. We need to think about ways in which we can disrupt outdated methods of delivering instruction to make way for methods that encourage full participation by students in class. We want to give students the opportunity to create information together as they assemble meaning and apply new knowledge in situated contexts. In short, we need to be thinking about how we can help students and teachers to use technology to create more meaningful learning experiences that prepare students for their lives in the twenty-first century.

Developing Design Requirements Based on Research Findings

Modern learning spaces encompass a diverse variety of communication channels, some supported through technology and others - such as non-verbal gestures - accommodated by the physical organization of a room. The 'augmented reality' of a modern physical learning space needs to incorporate technology-supported communications alongside traditional communication in a way that blends the two in a seamless and coherent manner. Understanding the nature and impact of both forms of communication in learning experiences is a critical factor in developing appropriate technology systems.

Tidebreak's work is rooted in an understanding of pioneering work that resulted in modern computer interface conventions as well as more recent research findings related to human collaboration. Whereas Vannevar Bush posited the desktop metaphor that predicted the architecture of the personal computer,[3] and Douglas Englebart's team devised the Windows-Icons-Menus-Pointer interface (WIMP) that augmented the work of individuals,[4] Tidebreak is working to develop interface concepts that augment the collaborative work of teams.

The ideas behind Tidebreak's technologies were first developed as part of the 'iSpace' research project at Stanford University, which sought to explore the following question: 'What happens if a room itself becomes a computer interface?' During 1999-2004 researchers explored the nature of interactive workspaces - physical rooms augmented by installed technology systems as well as personal mobile devices - and how they might serve the needs of collaborative groups. In conjunction with technology development, researchers deployed early prototypes of systems and devices and studied the impact they had on teams engaged in real collaborative work, in particular engineering design. The coupling of technology development and work practice studies resulted in systems tuned to the realistic needs of collaborating teams as well as a deeper understanding of the future of work and learning.

Designing for Group-Users and Distributed Cognition

Groups of students working together engage in 'distributed cognition'. Whereas individual cognition pertains to processing by one person, in distributed cognition each member of a team brings with them a component of the cognitive capabilities of a team, as well as a different wealth of experiences and knowledge that can serve the needs of the group. Diverse teams often perform better than others because they bring a broader set of experiences and perspectives to bear on any task.[5] Learning space technology systems need to embrace and amplify this diversity by enabling a fluid flow of ideas and the active participation of all participants.

One of the key insights that came from the iSpace research was the notion of designing experiences for the 'group-user'.[6] As opposed to designing with a single user in mind and focusing on that user's interactions with technology for individual tasks, a group-user approach considers that individuals must successfully communicate ideas to others in a way that not only delivers the intended message, but also inspires the intended response or learning outcome.

Designing learning-space systems to support group users is an important goal for modern learning spaces, yet it is one that is becoming more of a challenge. Now that classroom technology systems comprise both standardised installed components (e.g., large displays, microphone systems, embedded computers) as well as a wide variety of mobile devices that students and instructors carry into the classroom, learning space technologies need to be as flexible - and as accommodating of multiple device platforms - as possible. At the same time, they need to deliver appropriate capabilities that advance the state-of-the-art in teaching and learning.

Realizing the Promise of Mobile Devices and BYOD Environments

The ubiquity of mobile devices provides a basis for putting powerful interaction capabilities into the hands of students, to draw them into active participation in learning activities. By interfacing these devices with installed classroom systems, it is possible to extend the capabilities of mobile devices, both for their owners and in helping to mediate communications among members of a group.

Learning spaces are effectively becoming peripheral accessories to the mobile devices that students and faculty carry with them. Tablets and smartphones are optimized to help consume information – through visiting websites, viewing photos, reading ebooks, etc. Their form also makes them attractive as content presentation devices. To date, much of the conversation related to mobile devices in classrooms has focused on how to allow instructors (or students) to stream presentations in class, or how to make personal annotations associated with a presentation that is being broadcast to a larger group. Unfortunately these are limited capabilities that reinforce traditional teacher-centric, presentation-focused instructional approaches.

The real potential for using mobile devices lies in their role as highly portable and reconfigurable gateways to information and communication. If it is made possible for students and instructors to access web content and then immediately send copies of the content directly to a screen in the classroom - rather than a video stream of the device screen - mobile devices can be employed to tap the distributed cognition of the group while students explore new ideas interdependently. Individuals can follow different paths of inquiry and then ultimately share their findings for discussion much more quickly than if one person led the group in its explorations. If students are allowed to use mobile devices to control the content once it appears on large displays in the room, they can be drawn more extensively into related activities. And if a record is kept of all the content shared by members of the group and saved in a single location that is accessible in real-time during class or offline afterwards, a collection will be built of the digital artefacts that are shared during the exchange of ideas. Together these capabilities can create an environment in which students can participate fully because they are empowered to manage content together. Implementing these capabilities across devices and installed systems requires a new infrastructure approach for learning spaces.

Embracing Software-centric Technology Infrastructures

The value of interaction systems will increasingly be embedded in the software that runs on standardised computing hardware, as opposed to proprietary AV hardware systems that have been the basis for most technology-based classrooms for decades. AV switches and custom-programmed control-systems hardware will be replaced by middleware software systems that run over the IT network on standards-based devices. These middleware technologies will bind together heterogeneous hardware systems (e.g., mobile devices, interactive display screens, laptops and whiteboard capture systems) and wrap interaction capabilities around existing software applications.

There are several desirable advantages to using a software infrastructure:

- Any device on the network can be joined to the infrastructure to become a source or receiver of content and interaction. This means equal access to interaction for all individuals.
- Customised preferences can be configured in software - for instance, designating different levels of interaction access for faculty and students.
- Systems can be immediately reconfigured to reflect changes in organisation of a class for group work.
- Major software upgrades can be deployed using standard-enterprise disc-management tools.
- Standardised computer hardware can be upgraded at lower cost to boost performance while maintaining the same user experience without requiring custom programming.
- Meta-interface applications built on top of the middleware infrastructure can provide a cohesive, unified interface experience for the installed system and can also avoid the 'silo' effect in which different products do not interoperate.

In sum, the shift to a software infrastructure will eliminate many hardware-induced constraints, ease upgrade and scalability, and provide powerful new capabilities for interactive learning spaces.

Promoting the Adoption of New Best Practices

An important consideration associated with new technologies is how to encourage adoption and develop best practices. Students are likely to embrace new interactive learning capabilities facilitated through technology, but they may not necessarily develop best practices without guidance from instructional staff. It will be the responsibility of instructors to help students appreciate the benefits of collaborative work for their future professional pursuits, benefits that include: democratising participation, encouraging deep discussion of material as it is developed, and promoting greater alignment amongst the group related to their work product.

Instructors themselves are likely to require coaching on adopting new approaches in order to overcome inertia associated with existing practices. Instructors often become more motivated once they experience the benefits of engaging students in the co-creation of learning experiences both within and outside the classroom.

The evolution of best practices benefits from a combination of grass-roots and top-down programmes. Grass-roots demand from students who are exposed to new technologies in one context and want to see them more broadly applied will call attention to new techniques and will encourage adoption. Top-down support through incentive structures and other forms of leadership commitment will drive institutionalisation. In both cases, some degree of patterning will be required at multiple levels to illustrate how to create more interactive environments, either through technology or in conjunction with it.

Looking to the Future

The transformation of learning spaces from presentation-focused to interaction-focused environments is in its early stages, but the transformation is taking place at many institutions. BYOD (Bring Your Own Device) considerations and a resurgence of active learning pedagogies are driving the development of new forms of learning space and associated technology capabilities. While traditional AV systems continue to be deployed in some classrooms, financial considerations and technology change associated with the migration to mobile computing are making it increasingly difficult to justify old design paradigms. This bodes well for encouraging institutions to embrace paradigm shifts that will increase student engagement within learning spaces.

Campuses today are augmented-reality environments in which real and digital worlds meet. The design challenge is to preserve the richness of non-technical experiences while developing a technology-based approach that extends the physical learning environments of students and instructors in appropriate ways to enhance their shared experiences. In this, interactivity will be an important dimension to which campuses will need to attend.

However, innovative solutions are unlikely to emerge by extrapolating from the design of traditional learning spaces. Forward-looking institutions will need to take a leadership role to promote their vision, to introduce new ideas using existing technologies, and to work collaboratively with technology providers - such as Tidebreak - to prepare new tools and techniques that serve teaching and learning needs in the years to come.

Tidebreak™

References

1.   Milne, A.J. (2007). 'Entering the Interaction Age: Implementing a Future Vision for Campus Learning Spaces – Today'. EDUCAUSE Review, vol. 42, pp. 12–31.

2.   Milne, A.J., Leifer, L. (2000). 'Information Handling and Social Interaction of Multi-disciplinary Design Teams in Conceptual Design: A Classification Scheme Developed from Observed Activity Patterns'. Proceedings of the ASME Design Theory and Methodology Conference, Baltimore, MD.

3.   Bush, V. (1945). 'As We May Think'. The Atlantic Monthly, vol. 176, pp. 101-108
4.   Engelbart, D.C. (1995) 'Toward Augmenting the Human Intellect and Boosting our Collective IQ'. Communications of the ACM, vol. 38 p. 30.

5.   Carrillo, A. (2002). 'Engineering Design Team Performance: Quantitative Evidence that Membership Diversity Effects are Time Dependent', Ph.D. dissertation, Stanford University.

6.   Milne, A.J. (2005). 'An Information-Theoretic Approach to the Study of Ubiquitous Computing Workspaces Supporting Geographically Distributed Engineering Design Teams as Group-Users', Ph.D. dissertation, Stanford University.

Chapter 6

Using Visualisers

Duncan Peberdy

Large-scale lectures and presentations designed to communicate information and knowledge have a major drawback: they take for granted that all audience members will achieve a similar understanding. In today's universities, which cater for larger student populations with a greater breadth of academic abilities, it is unrealistic to expect similar levels of understanding. Yet despite the advent of active learning, universities are not going to dispense with lectures and lecture theatres. Even new campuses under construction are being configured with substantial capacity for lectures. For example, the Great Hall of Swansea University's new Bay Campus includes large-capacity lecture theatres.

The Application of Visualisers to Lectures

Students today seem to require constant stimulation. They find it difficult to concentrate on one thing for even 15 minutes. More than ever before, good teaching needs to engage and challenge students, motivating them to pay attention and think for themselves.

Visualisers provide lectures with an alternative means of presentation to PowerPoint slides which can engage or re-engage students' attention. Whereas a PowerPoint slide might depict a theoretical situation, a visualiser can provide the opportunity to show a real-life example, be it something medical, mechanical, or artistic. Standing behind a visualiser and facing students, a lecturer can make and maintain eye-contact with students, gauging their reactions and responding accordingly. With the right visualiser, an academic can even add real-time annotations to an object, or record student feedback, which will provide students with invaluable contextual memory tags when they review captured learning as part of revision before examinations.

At Warwick Business School some lecture theatres and teaching rooms are equipped with WolfVision visualisers and TOP-TEC lecterns specifically designed as writing surfaces. When a lecturer needs to add real-time written information or expand an explanation, instead of turning away from the students and using a flip chart or dry erase board, he or she can retain eye contact and work on a large surface. The visualiser captures the lecturers work and replicates it on a large screen. Diagrams and objects - even small ones - can be placed on the lectern surface and displayed, and there is room for annotations to be added or student feedback to be recorded. The optical quality of WolfVision equipment is powerfully demonstrated when, at the push of a button in the lectern, a Visualiser focuses on a minute detail. It can provide students with stunning crystal-clear large format representations.

An example of a TOP-TEC lectern with an A2 dry-wipe writing area developed for use with the WolfVision VZ-3s Visualiser.

How students would view the content

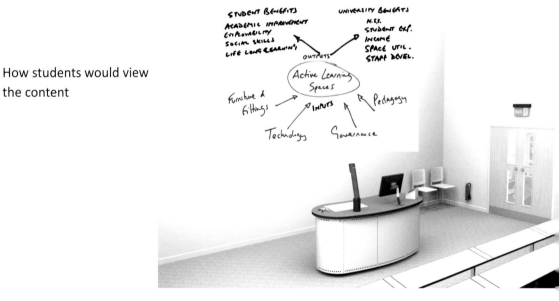

Visualisers are also more flexible than PowerPoint presentations because a lecturer can engage students in an ad-lib way. A mixture of different methods (PowerPoint, video, and visualisers) can also be used. This provides students with a positive experience by reducing the intellectual overload that occurs when just a single presentation format is used exclusively.

Many small lecture theatres and seminar rooms in universities are equipped with dual projection displays. In the vast majority of these rooms there are no viewing restrictions yet identical information is shown on both screens, which are positioned next to each other. Such an arrangement is a waste of opportunity for engaging better with students by showing additional visual information. It would be advantageous for universities to go further and invest in visualisers.

Given the value that visualisers provide for students and lecturers, Visualisers they should be employed in every lecture.

Sketch of a Lecture Theatre at Warwick Business School where a WolfVision ceiling-mounted Visualiser captures and displays the content from a dry-wipe surface in a TOP-TEC Lectern.

PART 2
Creating and Managing Learning Spaces

Chapter 7

Student Expectations of Buildings and Facilities
Duncan Peberdy

Not long ago, most university learning took place in lecture theatres, seminar rooms and libraries. In lecture theatres a single academic transferred knowledge to numerous students; seminar rooms contained formal arrangements of furniture; and libraries provided opportunities for individual learning.

Since the early twenty-first century, as mobile computing and connecting technologies have provided greater flexibility, the characteristics of learning spaces have developed, notably with the provision of social spaces in libraries, café areas, etc.   The CETL (Centres for Excellence in Teaching and Learning) programme throughout England has focused a discussion about how students learn – with emphasis on visual and collaborative approaches and on the spaces and technology academics require to fulfil new learning strategies or scenarios.

The Day The World Changed: 3 April 2010
An event that happened on this day has changed for-ever the way in which universities deliver education. For many years, wireless laptops provided mobility of work and learning for millions of people. But the introduction of Apple's iPad in April 2010 raised mobility to a new level. The functionality of the iPad, and of similar devices such as the Samsung Galaxy Note, Microsoft Surface Pro 2, together with the availability of numerous free or low-cost third-party software applications (apps), now provide almost everything needed for the educational and social lives of undergraduates: internet access, music, videos, games, touch screen with virtual keyboard, long battery life, and more. Students now have devices that can be taken anywhere and used productively in almost any situation. Apple has created a world in which wireless access is the expectation, and for which manufacturers of screens, projectors and other devices have provided the content of personal devices to be easily shared with larger groups.

Students expect to use their personal devices everywhere - at home, on trains, in coffee shops, and for learning on campus. So unless their studies involve specialist hardware or expensive software requiring high processing power or complex connections, students require spaces in which their own computing equipment can be used. That increasingly means supporting two or three mobile devices per student - smartphone, tablet, laptop, etc.

The Bay Campus of Swansea University, for example, has been designed with sufficient Wi-Fi bandwidth to support three devices per student.

In parts of the UK these technological developments roughly coincide with the introduction of substantially higher tuition fees for many students. It has therefore become essential for universities to provide students with perceived value for money.   For school leavers the choice of a university usually involves assessment of teaching facilities. So the quality of buildings and their learning spaces is a vital consideration for universities seeking to attract students who can connect for learning at any time from any place.

Intention and Execution

While the importance of providing high-quality buildings and learning spaces is clear, the design and construction of facilities can be difficult and the outcomes often flawed. Buildings sometimes have rooms with ceilings too low for the proper positioning of projected images or walls cluttered with switches, alarms and access controls which reduces the areas in which multiple displays can be show. Sometimes power and data connections are situated in the wrong place.

One source of such difficulties is the tendency for modern contracts to minimise – or even remove – the architect from the physical construction process. The construction process stresses the need for work to be on time and within budget at the expense of academic-related considerations. A professor of architectural design at a leading UK University has commented:

> 'I wouldn't argue against the need for buildings which are delivered on time and within budget, but I am concerned that in focusing on these criteria we sometimes fail to address other aspects sufficiently well.   As a result we may have buildings built to the agreed completion date and cost, but they may be deeply flawed in other aspects of their design. As a result they may eventually prove far worse value for money than alternatives which were dismissed or overlooked due to the failings of those involved in the design of the building.

> My observation is that the design process is itself often very poorly designed. One cause of this can be insufficient consultation with user groups. Good management would hopefully ensure arrangements for a suitable design process were in place at the outset of any project.'

Lessons from the Corporate World

Modern formal active learning spaces can be viewed as the educational equivalent of corporate meeting rooms. It can also be argued that higher education could learn much from the advances made by commercial organisations in collaborative working with clients and colleagues. Persuaded by extensive research by workplace specialists such as Steelcase and Herman Miller, some companies have invested in radical redevelopment of their working spaces to achieve the kind of benefits that universities are now seeking from new learning spaces. Developments have included the clustering of facilities, complete Wi-Fi coverage including guest provision, and dropdown zones in which guests find facilities that make them welcome and comfortable on arrival (toilets, refreshments, power, Wi-Fi). Such arrangements encourage people to arrive early for appointments, because they can be comfortable and productive while they wait. For staff, they avoid narrow restrictive corridors, providing circulation space for individual contemplation or ad-hoc group conversations including the use of technology. Eating and drinking areas mostly resemble coffee shops, allowing people to consume refreshments or hold informal meetings. The latter have proved to advance business.

If universities want to attract students in the first place and retain them on campus for as long as possible, they must provide social learning spaces in which activities found in the corporate world can be replicated.

Chapter 8

Project Planning and Technical Installations
Duncan Peberdy

Technical installations for new and refurbished spaces typically require many months of planning. For example, large screens require considered positioning, careful cabling, efficient control from a lectern, high-quality accompanying audio, and provision for many different inputs (computer, video, video conferencing, network, etc.). Standards for AV (audio visual) installations worldwide have been drawn up by InfoComm, who also provide training and certification across the industry - from manufacturers to consultants to installation experts. The standards specify, for example, the size of projection screen that should be fitted into a lecture theatre in relation to the distance from the front to the furthest seat, thus ensuring that content can be clearly seen from the back and is not overpowering at the front. Similar considerations apply to the height of the screen: those at the back should be able to see the entire screen, without any obstruction from the heads of those in front.

Buildings and rooms can easily be designed without consideration for the technical equipment that is due to be installed. An architect for example, might design a low ceiling because he or she loves the feeling of warmth that it provides. But this might mean that there is now insufficient height for a large screen to be installed. If only the architect had consulted an AV specialist at an early stage.

An AV team at a university became so fed up by a lack of consultation in the planning stages for new or refurbished learning spaces that they drew up guidelines. Some extracts are reproduced below.

'This section covers requirements for IT and AV installations in teaching rooms and student open access areas.

1. **Project Planning – early stages**
   Involvement of IT Services at the earliest stage possible is vital so that the team are able to contribute specialist technical knowledge to the planning and implementation of excellent solutions. This must include preliminary sight of plans (even if subject to change) together with a briefing on proposed room usage and special requirements. Sufficient information must be provided at the early stages to allow IS to research technical solutions where necessary, and give guide cost estimates for input into the project plan. Information Services must be advised whenever any changes are made to plans that impact IT or AV installations in any way.

   IS will work with the project team to identify the optimum equipment for the space allocated.

   If, at project inception, there are any plans for the integration of new AV technologies that are not currently in use at the University, then IS must be consulted immediately so that a proper assessment can be made as to whether the plan is feasible and supportable. If IS (after wider consultation) decide otherwise, then the technology will not be deployed but IS will provide a suitable alternative for integration into the plan. Early stage involvement before plans are finalised will also eliminate such issues as low ceilings, poor sightlines to projection screen and other areas which may impact the smooth operation of AV installation.

2. Project planning – detail stages

IT Services must have detailed and accurate project phase dates to aid planning, purchasing and installations. If alterations have been made to the early plans that in any way impact the IS peripheral installation, IS must be informed and included in any discussions or sign off meetings.

If IS consider plans compromise the IT/AV usability or will result in a poor staff or student experience, then suitable constructive comments and suggestions will be made. In extreme circumstances, if a layout is planned that is not functional then IS will decline to continue with the installation. The issue must then be escalated for resolution.'

Many small and large rooms have been created whose functionality for learning was compromised because essential AV equipment were the last elements to be considered. Policy-makers must consult with all stakeholders for a project from the outset if students are to be provided with great facilities. Inadequate AV facilities have the potential to damage a university's reputation.

There are two organisations in the UK Higher Education sector whose members are involved in planning and equipping learning spaces:

1.   Standing Conference for Heads of Media Services (SCHOMS). This is a professional body for senior managers whose remit is 'Designing and developing new learning environments and deploying learning technologies'.

2.   Learning and Teaching Spaces Managers Group (LTSMG). This is dedicated to the continual improvement of teaching spaces and teaching aids.

Chapter 9

Integrating Student Perspectives into the Development of Learning Spaces at the University of Lincoln

Sam Williams

Space Planning and Strategy Manager, University of Lincoln

The University of Lincoln has played a significant role in the development of learning space design in higher education. From 2008 to 2010 it led a national research project in collaboration with international design company DEGW and eleven other British universities: Edinburgh Napier, Glasgow, Glyndwr, Newcastle, Loughborough, Oxford Brookes, Queen Mary (London), Reading, Warwick, Wolverhampton and York. The project explored ways in which academics work with colleagues in estates departments and other key stakeholders to develop and manage innovation in the design of teaching and learning spaces in higher education. Its final report was published in April 2010 and is available from Lincoln University's Learning Landscapes website[1].

The project generated ten key principles for the effective design and development of learning spaces. They are now formally embedded at Lincoln, on every level from the campus masterplan[2] to the specification of individual pieces of furniture. They are as follows:

1. Drive research into effective teaching and learning.
2. Provide support models for staff and students on how to use innovative spaces, with provision for mentoring.
3. Include students, as clients and collaborators, ensuring their voices are heard.
4. Evaluate spaces in ways that are academically credible, based on measures of success that reflect the kinds of activities that are taking place.
5. Understand the importance of time as an issue for space planning: not just space, but space-time.
6. Connect the learning and teaching space with the campus as a whole, in ways that articulate the vision and mission of the university.
7. Recognise and reward leadership that supports the development of learning and teaching spaces.
8. Create formal and informal management structures that support strategic experimentation.
9. Clarify roles, grounded in supportive relationships between and across professional groups.
10. Intellectualise the issues: generate debate on the nature of academic values and the role and purpose of higher education: the idea of the university.

In her 2009 paper Space Strategies for the New Learning Landscape[3], Shirley Dugdale of DEGW (now Principal at Dugdale Strategy LLC) emphasised the need to analyse the whole campus as potential learning space, and she identified three key trends in the area of learning space demand:

1. Traditional categories of space are becoming less meaningful as activities blend, space becomes less specialized, boundaries between disciplines blur, and operating hours extend toward 24/7 access.

2. In the future, space types are more likely to be designed around patterns of human interaction than around the specific needs of particular departments, disciplines, or technologies.

3. With greater mobility, students have a choice in where they can work and tend to gravitate to spaces they enjoy - so quality of design matters more. New space models for educational institutions therefore need to focus on enhancing quality of life as well as supporting the learning experience.

To these could be added the inexorable rises in student expectations and property costs, which squeeze the university estate from opposite directions, often requiring spaces to do double or triple duty throughout the university day, week and year while performing superbly in at least one role; and the blurring of the traditional distinctions between the learning environment and the world of work, as university employers and professional support staff both recognise the imperative for continuous learning and development throughout careers which will soon span at least 50 years.

New Learning Environments

At Lincoln, the Learning Landscapes principles have been applied to the development of new learning environments across the campus, notably in the design of the David Chiddick Building (2010) for the university's schools of Business and Law, in the remodelling and extension of the University Library (2011, 2013), in the transformation of the Main Administration Building[4] (2012, 2013), in the new Joseph Banks Laboratories[5] (2014), and in the design of outdoor social and learning spaces which connect the academic and residential buildings.

As the UK government's Commission for Architecture and the Built Environment has articulated so clearly, the greatest opportunity to influence a project's outcome is at, or even before, project initiation.[6] Universities and suppliers who wish to understand and respond comprehensively to students' and academics' needs must not rely on the limited form of engagement possible within individual projects, which are inherently time-limited and resource-constrained. Continuous research and dialogue in anticipation of future project requirements, as well as rigorous evaluation of recent projects, are key requirements for long-term success.

The Learning Landscapes team at Lincoln therefore developed a set of interlocking formal and informal management structures to support strategic experimentation and evaluation concerning learning spaces during and between projects. They included:

1. Formation of an interdisciplinary Learning Spaces Group which brought together

academics, students, estates, timetabling and IT professionals to plan, implement and evaluate new spaces.

2. Creation and maintenance of a website through which Learning Landscapes projects, events and research are shared with students, staff and the public, along with active use of social media to promote and invite comment on developments.[7]

3. Expansion of pre-existing committees to include regular formal reporting and discussion of Learning Landscapes progress (notably the university's Education and Student Experience committees).

4. Staging a series of Learning Landscapes conferences and workshops attended by students and staff from Lincoln and other universities.

All of these structures are intended to engage students and academics continuously as co-creators of the new learning landscape in line with the university's core organising principle for teaching and learning: Student as Producer[8]. The website serves as a meta-structure, drawing the whole programme together and making it visible.

The work of Professor Peter Jamieson, Strategic Advisor for Learning Environment Design at the University of Melbourne, has been a constant touchstone for the Learning Landscapes team at Lincoln. Professor Jamieson's conceptual framework for the creation of new-generation learning environments has inspired numerous projects and processes at Lincoln. Professor Jamieson's approach emphasises inclusive design in which students and academics employ spatial and cultural metaphors from outside higher education to imagine new spaces.

Learning from Students

One of our most fruitful engagement activities was a workshop on seminar room design at the university's Student-Staff Conference in February 2013. This is an annual event, crucially organised not by the corporate university but by the Students' Union. Facilitated by the university's space planning team, who had been invited to run a session by the SU's vice-president for academic affairs, a group of 15 students and staff used memories and metaphors to generate a set of socio-spatial factors which would support an ideal seminar experience, and then to imagine new types of learning spaces. The aim of the hour-long session was to engage students and staff in 'talking our future into being', informing the design of future refurbishment and construction projects. The workshop is documented on the Learning Landscapes website[9].

After dividing the group into four student-staff subgroups, we first asked participants to recall their best seminar experience and to consider: what made it great? what were they doing physically during the seminar? what was the impact it had on them? and was the room a factor? We then asked each subgroup to distinguish the factors involved in a great seminar. The responses could be broadly characterised as either spatial or social:

Spatial Factors

Open environment
Acoustics
Ease of movement
Movable furniture
Flexibility of room
Toys to play with
No barriers: no desks at the front
Good lighting
Less distraction
Appropriate temperature: not too cold
Furniture design: flexibility

Social Factors

People talking
Small Groups
Ability to get involved
Lecturer sat with us
More participation
Group involvement
Better understanding
Encouraging conversation

There was a strikingly high level of consensus among the four subgroups, despite the demographic and academic diversity of participants, who represented the university's three academic colleges and professional support staff. The above list of factors instantly became a key reference point for future seminar room design at Lincoln.

We began a second exercise at the workshop by explaining our design process for a set of recently completed seminar rooms. It had employed a metaphor drawn from outside higher education as advocated by Peter Jamieson. When we started to design the rooms in 2012, we drew inspiration from the recently completed McLaren Production Centre in Surrey. That facility features small groups of people working on complex processes at multiple locations; an extremely flexible layout which enables the whole space to be rearranged rapidly; and a calming, neutral colour palette with few visual distractions. We explained how each of these key features had translated to corresponding design decisions in the new learning spaces.

Having shared an example of metaphor-based design which had led to real seminar spaces, we gave the four subgroups about 15 minutes to come up with their own metaphors for new seminar spaces, using mobile whiteboards in each corner of the room to sketch and document their ideas. The subgroups generated four great concepts, each representing quite a distinct realm of experience:

1. The Bubble:
a cocoon-like outdoor seminar space with transparent sides and ethically sourced components and materials.

2. The Living Room:
a homely, relaxing place with sofa groups, table lamps and televisions for each subgroup.

3. The Airport:
a spacious, dynamic, technology-rich concourse within which users move between various seating and standing zones.

4. The Paw Print:
a sophisticated café-like space with group tables arranged in an arc round a central focal point.

The concepts were received with great enthusiasm by the university. In summer 2013, less than six months after the conference, three of the four concepts were implemented within a suite of new formal and informal learning environments on the upper levels of our Main Administration Building. The new spaces proved very popular, because of their design and their attractive location on and near pre-existing circulation routes.

By documenting the workshop publicly and referencing it in subsequent project communications, the university 'closed the loop' so that not only the workshop participants but also the wider University community could see the tangible results from the student-led design of learning environments. This happened fast enough to benefit many of the same students who had generated those concepts.

The 'student as producer' approach demonstrates the strategic value of organising deep student engagement in campus development, as in many other facets of the institution. Experience shows that genuinely empathic solutions are required and will be rewarded, not just in the physical design of new spaces but also in the political spaces in which decisions about the future of the campus are formed. Inclusive design approaches employing universal skills such as memory and metaphor can recruit 'non-designers' to conceptualise outstanding new learning environments. However, in order to harness students' talents fully, traditional decision-makers within the institution must be willing to relinquish some of their power. Just as students venture deeper into co-production of the learning environment, colleagues and suppliers involved in the design of new learning spaces must also cross the transom to become students themselves.

References:
1. http://learninglandscapes.blogs.lincoln.ac.uk/research
2. http://learninglandscapes.blogs.lincoln.ac.uk/masterplan
3. https://net.educause.edu/ir/library/pdf/ERM0925.pdf
4. http://learninglandscapes.blogs.lincoln.ac.uk/projects/mab-third-floor
5. http://learninglandscapes.blogs.lincoln.ac.uk/projects/joseph-banks-laboratories
6. http://webarchive.nationalarchives.gov.uk/20110118095356/http://www.cabe.org.uk/buildings/client-role
7. http://learninglandscapes.blogs.lincoln.ac.uk
8. http://studentasproducer.lincoln.ac.uk
9. http://learninglandscapes.blogs.lincoln.ac.uk/engage/studentstaff-conference-2013

Chapter 10

Maximising Value from the Physical Environment

Cathy Rex
Director of Library Services, University of the West of England

Physical space is normally the largest cost for any university after its staff budget. But however well a university's physical estate is designed and refurbished, the university will not get best value if organisational and behavioural issues are not also addressed. This requires top-level direction combined with acceptance of involvement and responsibility by staff.

In 2007 the UK Higher Education Space Management Project sponsored by the UK funding councils for HE was finished and 'Implementing SMG Guidance' was published.[1] It outlined a check-list of 14 questions. The report 'emphasises that space management should not be viewed solely as an "estates" issue. Instead, it needs to be carefully integrated with institutions' strategic and financial planning. Strong leadership and organisation, combined with good, up-to-date information on estate performance, underpin successful space management.'

When academic staff were asked what they wanted with regard to provision of teaching space, they replied:

- IT that works (IT want staff to turn up for training)
- a clean space
- an environment (heating, lighting etc.) that can be controlled or at least is comfortable
- to be timetabled for a space with the appropriate furniture and equipment
- to be timetabled for a space with sufficient accommodation for the students involved
- IT that supports the teaching
- flexible space (but without undue need to move furniture)
- timetabled space designed for active learning

These points are a combination of space-management and design issues. The list illustrates the need for management systems that aid the design, maintenance and development of the learning environment, including the AV (audio visual) and IT kit. Without this, any improvement derived from investment will be limited and brief. Various relationships must function properly if a physical estate is going to support learning and teaching effectively.

Strategic Planning

Teaching space must be designed so as to support academic strategy. If the strategy is clear and informs the design brief then an institution is more likely to be successful. If an institution espouses active learning, space design has to take into account technology and appropriate furniture design. This requires much more involvement by staff with technical and specialist expertise than was necessary for designing 'traditional' spaces. New technology brings with it great functionality but also new costs and decisions.

To ensure that an estate remains fit for purpose, space planning and investment need to be kept constantly under review. This includes evaluation of any new spaces for a lengthy period so that their use can be refined and experience can inform future developments. Furniture and equipment must also be monitored to ensure that technology is updated and chairs and other furniture are replaced as they become worn out. A maintenance schedule is desirable to keep the decoration of rooms refreshed (including carpets) and to ensure that infrastructure remains in good working order (e.g. heating, lighting). This requires robust methods of gathering information to inform decision-making, and good management and budgetary planning.

Good information is required to ensure that demand for and availability of facilities are matched. Managers need the right number of rooms of the right size, with the right equipment to meet academic requirements, taking into account the timetabled day and student numbers. If there is a mismatch then problems will arise despite timetablers' best efforts. Where there are specialist requirements (e.g. media studios, science laboratories) this is especially important. Agility is required in managing space to fit needs. This will only happen successfully if the demands on space are known and understood and trends are analysed.

Ownership by all Staff

Top-level direction alone will not deliver an effective learning environment. Everybody has a part to play. But it is essential to have a common goal and for participants to understand their role in achieving it. The ideal scenario is for teaching spaces to be developed by teams of staff drawn from organisational units, who can contribute their knowledge in pursuit of a common objective – a space that meets the operational need. Estates, AV and IT staff need to envisage the space through the eyes of academics and students; academic staff need to understand the operational constraints that will influence the design. Academic staff also need to explain how a space will enable or constrain interaction with students and how this will affect student learning.

Regular communication and staff development must also be provided to maximise that accrue from significant investment in learning environments. This can include the initial provision of pilot spaces for evaluating the impact of a new technology or layout. Findings should then be incorporated in planning and the evolution of specifications.

Flexible Spaces

In designing teaching spaces, so-called 'flexible spaces' should not be seen as planning for specific needs. It can prove costly to invest in flexibility and adaptability and discover later that they are never used because they were not required. Examples of unnecessary provision include moveable walls and very high technical specification for spaces in which there will be little use of technical equipment. Multiple-use, flexible spaces can also mask a mismatch in supply and demand, and compromise quality where there is an operational incompatibility between different uses. Space designed to support multiple functions can turn out to be fit for none of them.   It is worth remembering that, over time, the use and functionality of a room can often be altered fairly quickly and relatively cheaply, especially if this is done as part of a rolling cycle of upgrade and refreshment.

'Flexibility' has often meant the provision of furniture on wheels. This is a so-called 'intervention model' and requires the users of space to arrange the furniture to support different activities. In practice the use of furniture with wheels is inefficient. The time required to rearrange a room cannot be provided easily between sessions or within sessions. Rearrangement between days requires assistance from porters, which can be expensive. If tables are irregular in shape, rearrangement can be difficult. Rearranged rooms often look dishevelled. Imperfect wheel-lock mechanisms can also be impediments. In sum, it is unrealistic to require the rearrangement of rooms on a large scale.

On the other hand, rearrangement can work if rearranged furniture is left standing for relatively long periods. It is also convenient to use folding tables for occasional needs (e.g., catering in a foyer or for a one-off event.)

Behavioural Aspects and Managing Expectations

Instead of 'flexible spaces', it is more efficient for an institution to have a 'mixed economy' of different types of space with different sets of facilities. This allows different activities to be supported, but requires teachers to think about how they 'work' each type of space, and requires managers to guide teachers in booking the right space for their requirements. This is necessarily the case where a rigid AV system is installed. Effective space utilisation requires good management of expectations and people. For example, it is unrealistic for some to set a date and time for a meeting and then expect the ideal room to be available. Room availability should be factored into the timing of a meeting. This can be facilitated by ease of access to relevant room booking information.

This latter situation illustrates that many factors are involved in producing a good user experience and effective space utilisation. They include: compilation of information on supply and demand of spaces; management of staff expectations and behaviour; establishment of a systems to make it easy for people to follow the rules; ability to adapt spaces as supply and demand alter over time.

Room Design Standards

The approach to room provision and management outlined in this chapter are based on having suitable room design standards. Standards for timetabled rooms should be agreed in planning and based on pedagogic innovation. The provision of facilities and equipment at different levels should be thought out carefully to guard against oversupply of expensive provision – this includes AV and IT specifications.   A 'one- size fits all' approach to room provision will not succeed because requirements vary. Standards also need to be updated to reflect changes in demand and in technology.

Provision of choice allows staff and students to specify the space that best fits their functional requirements with which they feel comfortable. For this to work, room-booking and timetabling systems must be able to match rooms to activities, with staff specifying their requirements in advance. Staff must be able to find information easily about room configurations and how to book a suitable space. The correct mix room with different facilities will be required.

Day-to-day Management

However well teaching spaces are designed and managed, their effectiveness will be undermined if they are not kept clean and tidy, and if equipment is not in working order. Provision should be made for daily cleaning and checking of furniture layout. Use of space should be monitored and evaluated. Protocols need to be made to establish, for example, responsibility for cleaning white boards or reporting faults. They should be easy to understand and publicised.

Room Location and Clustering

Within an institution, not only do individual rooms have to be well designed, the clustering of rooms requires careful planning to create an effective larger environment. It doing this, it is critical to understand relationships between spaces and functions:

*   the way in which spaces support and relate to each other
*   the flow of activity through and between spaces
*   the total demand for use of a particular type of space and its best location
*   the potential for sharing space
*   the potential for clustering with similar functions (e.g. laboratories) to facilitate ancillary support

For some types of spaces location is crucial consideration. For example, a 'student learning zone' might be placed in an area with high footfall which is easy to find, and which is near toilets, catering, and other facilities for students. Locating it at the end of an obscure corridor at the top of a block would be unlikely to generate high use however good the design.

Design and Equipment of Rooms

If teaching rooms are to function well, they require good internal planning and equipping. This can easily be ruined by poor decisions. For example, a room intended for collaborative working by twenty students might be fitted out for twenty-five. As a result, table size is reduced to achieve a higher capacity. This affects personal space which reduces personal comfort. It also impairs the movement of staff and students within the space. Functionality is undermined, and engagement and learning suffer. If the room is used daily for eight periods, its deficiencies affect two hundred students a day.

Internal design and equipping should reflect the intended learning style for a room. Sustained use requires comfortable chairs, while collaborative working requires group tables. Contemplative working requires individual spaces, while specialist facilities may also be needed. It is important to have good information about the intended functions.

Systems should be created for sharing knowledge about, and experience of, how spaces are used, and about desirable improvements. Purchasing decisions require an amalgam of expertise. They should be pedagogically driven and informed, and combined with specialist knowledge about AV, IT and furniture. It is essential that design teams comprise of people with different expertise, who share their knowledge and develop a collective understanding of the physical environments that need to be created to support learning.

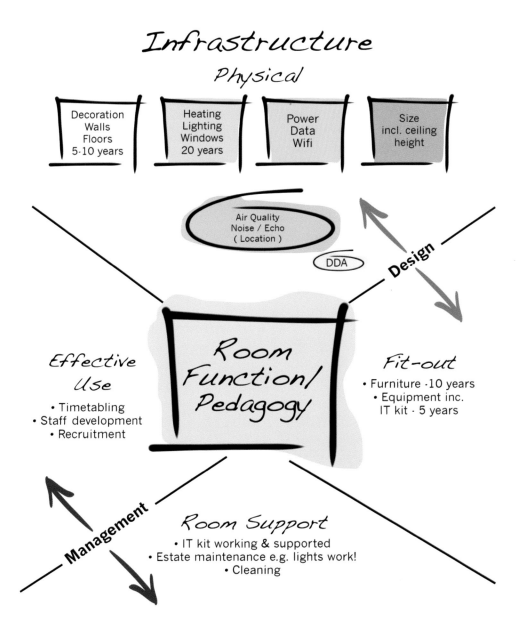

References:

1. 2007 the UK Higher Education Space Management Project, *Implementing SMG Guidance*: http://www.smg.ac.uk/documents/Implementing%20SMG%20Guidance%202007.pdf

Chapter 11

Scalability

Duncan Peberdy

Despite active learning spaces in the UK being in their infancy they are, nevertheless, creating significant interest. Not least because they are proving universally popular with the 'customers' of higher education that are exposed to these new teaching methodologies. The School of Pharmacy at The University of Bradford has produced an independent video – 'Introduction to Team Based Learning', available on YouTube – that documents the satisfaction of both staff and students who have used their Team Based Learning Room for the first year of their undergraduate studies. At Bradford and other universities where collaborative learning is available, it's not only the students who feel 'let down' when teaching takes place in traditional didactic-configured rooms. Those tutors who have volunteered to pioneer active learning are the ones that understand that with the correct facilities they can produce better learners, and who are then professionally frustrated when they are timetabled in 'normal' classrooms; active learning just doesn't work in those rooms.

Once students have experienced active learning spaces with the correct learning scenarios forming the basis for instruction, they quickly realise that there is a big difference between their experiences in these social rooms compared to what they have been used to. Who wouldn't want to have the best facilities all the time? But active learning spaces, with the technology that makes them really productive to learners, are more expensive to provide than traditional rooms, and transforming every room to an active learning room isn't something that will happen overnight.

Effective management of the complete university estate, with a strategy that involves all stakeholders, has become critical. Having just a few sporadic enhanced facilities that everyone wants to use can cause resentment, and will result in pinch-points where the supply of effectively equipped spaces doesn't meet student or staff demand. It would be very simplistic just to say that active learning spaces should be replicated across the campus, but given the complexity and expense of the technology that make them simple and intuitive to use for both learners and tutors, this will take time and involve long-term investment.

Where students begin to value group collaborative learning is in the formal spaces that support multiple team learning as a single cohort. Enthused by the enjoyment and achievement of working in groups, students look to continue group-working outside of formal sessions, and not having sufficient spaces to support this desired continuation of learning is reported by students time and time again as a major dissatisfaction. Spaces equipped for active learning need to be configured and managed in such a way that teams of students can access them for informal learning outside of formal tutor-led session. This now extends to the new-style 'connect-seating' lecture theatres developed by Nicolas Burwell at Burwell Deakins Architects that support both didactic teaching and active learning in the same space. Just as importantly, with the correct management, these lecture spaces can be used effectively by individual groups of students outside of formal teaching time.

In café areas, libraries and building foyers, introduction of multiple small-scale collaborative areas that students can access themselves in groups will also have a number of positive effects. With enough of them they will start to minimise the pinch-points – or possibly create some if there are not enough of them or if student access to them is poorly managed. So long as students have access to such spaces, they will keep students on-campus for longer, creating a greater bond between the university and the student, and winning more of the student's disposable spend for food, drink, etc. They further develop the social interaction of students engaged in group learning that help to prevent isolation; isolation which can ultimately result in students dropping out. Universities don't need to have many students drop out during their first year, for the lost income across subsequent years to have paid for more active learning spaces.

Effective management of these areas will help enormously. There are plenty of companies who offer resource scheduling, which would allow students to pre-book these ad-hoc facilities. This could be configured to limit students to a maximum amount of time, and perhaps require a minimum number of students to be present. Students report on the frustrations of wanting to use a table with three or four peers, only for it to be occupied by a single student.

Students increasingly bring their own computing equipment onto campus, the power of which is increasing. Universities that provide spaces where students can access their own equipment effectively, reduce the need to provide computing equipment and the space computer labs require. The cost of university-provided computing hardware and software can be swapped to the supply of active learning furniture and technology, and the cluster rooms where the fixed technology was located can also be re-assigned for other uses.

It's not uncommon for universities to invest in creating a 'flagship' space that becomes the focus for much media attention and the pivotal showcase on open days and for other high profile events. Sometimes the wow-factor veneer hides the reality of a space that looks great, but is functionally poor. Vanity projects with ultra-expensive technology, furniture and fittings fit for royalty should not be constructed at the expense of providing students with less spectacular surroundings, but ones which actually help them to move their learning forward. It is those functional facilities that are valued by students, and which are more likely to be replicated across the campus, providing the scalability that enhances N.S.S scores by being a positive influence on student outcomes.

Finally, it's all too easy to calculate the cost of providing these facilities across the campus, but more complicated to forecast the many costs of not doing so.

Synergy AirConnect - assisting campus-wide scalability

TOP-TEC manufactures a range of robust tables that are perfect for groups of six or fewer students to work collaboratively. The self-standing table frames support a display which the students use to share visual information. With the addition of an NEC display and Crestron's AirMedia wireless receiver, a student can sit at the table and share the content on their laptop, smartphone or tablet in just a few seconds. In fact, all the students can simultaneously connect, and change the image source from one student to another instantly, or display multiple pieces of information at the same time, which is perfect for when information needs to be compared and contrasted.

      With no wall or floor fixings, Synergy tables are perfect for adaptive spaces that need to be re-configurable to support different uses. For example a foyer that can feature multiple Synergy tables until required to host a graduation reception.

No fixed installation required

Supports BYOD
(Bring Your Own Device)

Maximises Space Utilisation

Helps Develop a campus-wide Active Learning Strategy

As mentioned earlier, students who cannot get access to these social learning areas invariable go off campus. The university jeopardises much needed income, and students feel frustrated and disappointed at best, especially if a number of them had agreed to meet in order to continue their learning together.

Available from April 2014:

Folding Synergy from TOP-TEC

Provides active learning spaces with the flexibility to:

    Share resources

    Remove so rooms can be used for examinations

    Remove so spaces can be used for large events

    Securely store

For more details on availability:

TOP-TEC - 0121 783 3838

PART 3
Active Learning Spaces

Chapter 12

Teaching in Active Learning Spaces

Duncan Peberdy

The carrot or the stick? Which learning approach would be better for students and make them more likely to engage? At a UK university attended by my nephew, so many students were not attending lectures that the stick approach was introduced: it was announced that students would automatically fail a module if they missed more than three lectures. Attendance rose, but this did nothing to improve the dullness of presentations in which PowerPoint slides read were pretty much verbatim for two hours. Instead, lecturers should engage students through active learning as a carrot. For a lecturer who has taught with the same deck of PowerPoint slides for five or ten years, transitioning to a different style of teaching might be daunting. Why change if lectures are well attended (albeit through compulsion) and if lecturers themselves were once taught in a similar way and yet have prospered?

To make matters more challenging, the teaching spaces which lecturers have become comfortable with are unsuitable for new active-learning methods, and the prospect of using more technology than a projector with automatic slider-advancer can be daunting. Somehow, lecturers and their managers have to break the cycle of 'doing things that were done to us'. That means being supported to overcome fear.

Active Learning Rooms

Active learning rooms (such as 'TEAL', 'SCALE-UP', 'TILE', 'TBL') visibly change the basis of teaching from information delivery from the front of a room to the use of individual tables of students working together.   To maximise the benefit of learner-centred education, students should receive preparatory work before they congregate to engage in active learning. As soon as students walk into an active learning environment, they instinctively know that their experience will be better than if they studied in a room with rows and columns of chairs.

Is This Active Learning?

There are a lot of misconceptions about active learning. Just presenting visual material or using interactivity does not make a session 'active'. Preparation for active learning can involve watching online content in advance, but this and the use of other online information does not constitute active learning.

Successful active learning requires considerable preparation by both tutors and students, and must be structured otherwise there will be much time-wasting. Active learning is designed to maximise the contact time between tutors and students, not to minimise it. It involves tutors pointing students in the right direction and ensuring that they have the necessary resources, but ultimately students should remain fully responsible for their own learning.

Meetings Workshop

If active learning seeks to prepare students for the world of work, then all students would benefit from a 'meetings workshop' at the start of their undergraduate studies: a short course that points out the consequences of arriving late, being unprepared, and not contributing fully. It would assist students to engage better with their studies, and make everyone understand the consequences of their actions for others.

Communication and Revelation

Once a university decides to consult about or introduce active learning, communication is crucial. Silence breeds 'Chinese Whispers', which can introduce misinformation and cause mistrust and ill-feeling. In advocating active learning, there is an impressive 'track record' to relate. It has improved students' studies and achievement. In fact, active learning should raise a university's ranking in the National Student Survey.

To obtain support from teaching staff for active learning it is useful to hold workshops or seminars. These could be organised and presented by an internal team (e.g., one responsible for professional development or technology enhanced learning or blended learning). Alternatively, outside experts could be employed, people already familiar with active learning implementations. They can use their real-life experiences to dispel myths and remove fears surrounding a totally different pedagogy. Another approach is to organise a small-scale pilot scheme and invite colleagues to observe active learning sessions in action. Teachers involved in the introduction of active learning often show concern about: additional preparation time required by active learning; pace of instruction (PowerPoint slides seem much easier to control); controlling visual technology for each team/table; provision of assessment and feedback. Many are also secretly concerned that a new style of teaching may expose weaknesses in their teaching capacity and knowledge of technology.

In autumn 2013 Nottingham Trent University (NTU) became the first UK university to pilot active learning across multiple schools, including Science and Technology, Art and Design, Business, and Law. In preparation, Professor Bob Beichner from North Carolina State University, the innovator and evangelist of the SCALE-UP programme for active learning, was invited to present a keynote lecture on his work and run workshops for NTU staff. The workshops were designed to mimic an active learning session, enabling staff to experience what their own students would encounter. Professor Beichner's enthusiasm for active learning was infectious and inspiring, and motivated NTU staff to consider actively how they could utilise active learning in their own teaching. He inspired an increase in the number of staff willing to join a pilot scheme.

Active Learning Scenarios

The purpose of active learning is to facilitate education in which students learn from and with each other. This means that they need to communicate verbally as they explore potential answers to challenges by mapping out ideas and concepts, solving problems, and explaining their thinking. Groups of students should be constructed purposely, with a range of academic abilities. In this way, all teams will be similar in composition. The less able will learn from the more able group members and the latter will themselves learn more by becoming informal tutors for the less able.

If active learning is to work successfully as a learning method and simultaneously nurture the skills required in today's working environments, there must be proper preparation and supervision. Teachers must set clear and achievable objectives. A good set is provided by the acronym 'SMART'.

Set tasks should be:

S   **Specific**

M   **Measurable**

A   **Achievable**

R   **Relevant**

T   **Time-bound**

If the objectives set for students encompass all of these elements, then there will be no confusion about requirements.

Each team member must remain accountable for his or her work and their contribution to the group. Situations must not be permitted whereby one or several members contribute little to outcomes. A danger with team work is that the loudest can become the most influential. But it is estimated that 35 to 50 per cent of the population are introverts, who often 'act' more extroverted to fit in. Active learning needs to accommodate multiple personality types and abilities, particularly the more introverted who, according to statistics, are the ones that achieve the best grades. Groups should assume responsibility for ensuring that everyone contributes. Teachers should also provide groups with frequent feedback on their work. This ensures that a topic has been fully understood before students proceed to the next one. This is especially important if understanding a topic is the basis for the next stage of study.

The work set for a group should require its members to discover new things such that they are developed academically and socially. Problem-solving, critical thinking and collaborative working will not be stimulated if a task is based on 'discovering' their existing knowledge. Active learning is never a test of already acquired knowledge, but a mind-stretching activity to discover something new.

Continuing Professional Development for University Teachers

University teaching is a curious profession, in that there is no mandatory continuing professional development. By contrast, the public would be unhappy if GPs practised without updating their skills and knowledge. When new facilities are installed at a university, typically as a pilot project, access can be restricted to teaching staff who have 'qualified' to use the facilities. This usually relates just to the technology. But for active learning, space, furniture and pedagogical knowledge are the most important ingredients; technology is just the 'icing on the cake'. Technology distributes information around a room, and gives students access to materials they need. But if technology becomes the focus, either because it fails to work or more likely a lecturer cannot operate it, then a teaching room's value is drastically reduced. It should be a disciplinary offence to provide or use an active learning space for standard lecture-style teaching. There is anecdotal evidence that teaching staff approaching retirement notably resist incorporating technology other than PowerPoint into their teaching. They should be required to undertake a development or be required to retire.

Professional Excellence: The University of Wolverhampton

The introduction of the LaTTE room (Learning and Teaching Test Environment) at the University of Wolverhampton, provides an excellent example of how to manage the introduction of active learning. For the first year, only staff who had undergone an induction session were allowed to use the facility. And for every lesson a learning technologist was present; they played a crucial role in the room's success. Firstly, they ensured that a lecturer was always able to use the technology effectively. For staff who had never previously taught in such a facility, it removed all worries about technology, allowing them to concentrate on their teaching.

But not every learning scenario or student engagement with the LaTTE room's technology and facilities worked. The learning technologists were more easily able than teachers to recognise shortcomings. These were reported in discussions about the room's effectiveness. The LaTTE room really was a test environment which Wolverhampton University was determined to learn from so that their expansion of active learning could be well informed from their own experience.

The Student Voice

An increase of teaching in active learning spaces is inevitable in the UK. As in the USA and Australia, the use of facilities for active learning has engaged and motivated students. As more of them experience active learning, they will increasingly become frustrated and demotivated by the continuing use of standard classrooms. As active learning gains more visibility, prospective students will prefer universities at which active learning is the norm rather than the exception.

Engaged and motivated students will not stop learning when a formal session ends. If the available teaching and social spaces are good, they will continue learning with their peers, making use of digital connections, VLEs and social media where appropriate. Teaching staff who ignore the benefits of active learning for students do so at their peril.

Chapter 13

Technology Considerations for Active Learning Spaces

Duncan Peberdy

Not long ago the audio visual elements used in teaching were limited to OHP, PowerPoint and projections from video recorders. But more recently lecture spaces have been developed for delivering high-definition images from a multitude of sources with audio of cinema quality. Live video and images from visualisers often augment presentations, and there is a growing trend for lectures to be recorded so they can be uploaded to virtual learning environments (VLEs) such as Blackboard or Moodle. Students who missed a lecture can now review it, together with real-time contextual interactions from students. Such recordings are vital if students want to revisit the content to reinforce their learning and for exam preparation.

Technology can now be used so flexibly and effectively in a lecture space that learning effectiveness can be improved without much additional spending. Many lecture theatres are equipped with two large displays with the intent that a main stream of information can be augmented with extra visual information. Much more important are visualisers. At their heart they replicate the functions of an OHP, but also provide zoom, image capture, object capture, audio capture, and connectivity to other devices. When linked to powerful projectors and large screens they provide bright large images. Lecturers who have become accustomed to teaching with OHPs find it difficult to adjust to life without them – there are anecdotes of lecturers retrieving OHPs from storage rooms and even skips after teaching rooms have been upgraded with visualisers. An OHP was simple to operate: the power was turned on and acetate sheets projected. Digital visualisers seem more troublesome, requiring connection to a computer, the launch of software, and ensuring that the projection works.

The transition from OHP to new technology requires provision for personal development. Unfortunately there is no formal continuing professional development across the university sector for teaching staff. For a profession that has already accommodated so much change this is surely scandalous. Moreover technology for improving learning and teaching cannot work without commitment from lecturers. Lecturers who understand technology, and use it to enhance rather than replace their teaching, are the future. So in a world in which technology changes and improves so rapidly, continuing professional development must be provided.

The introduction of new technology requires effective support for lecturers from learning technologists. They can assist a lecturer in a live situation so that he or she can be confident about working the equipment. Lecturers also need to be shown how information can be augmented to advance learning, how students can be engaged more effectively by correct use of equipment, and how the human dynamics of using a visualiser are better than turning your back to write on a whiteboard.

Visualisers are perfect for displaying objects, creating annotations, and providing live video feeds. They can even record the audio and visuals from a lecture, making learning sessions almost instantly available on a VLE. It isn't even necessary to stand next to a visualiser. For example, a visualiser can be controlled from a tablet PC as a lecturer roams around a, though effectiveness requires the preparation of content and learning scenarios in advance. When a lecturer finds a visualiser as easy to use as an OHP, he or she will soon realise how much more effective the equipment can be. Lecturers who are sufficiently self-motivated will quickly discover new ways to exploit the equipment's potential.

Most people intrinsically want to do the best job that they can, but often exhibit opposition to change. Unless teaching staff receive high-quality support, the fear of change will hold back the achievement of true progress. Change should be viewed positively, and those leading it should set the right expectations and provide the correct training and support. Change can be a problem because it unsettles people; but sometimes unsettling people gives them a fresh start.

Planning and Equipping New Spaces

Unless a new teaching method requires unusual facilities, the academics do not normally need to be concerned about the technical aspects of new or refurbished teaching rooms. These are determined by international and local standards for the provision of visual and audio equipment, which should ensure that simple but far-reaching mistakes are avoided. For example, if a screen is too large viewers will be unable to see everything without moving their heads; conversely, if it is too small text will be unreadable. If there are screens on more than one wall – an increasingly common arrangement – then the provision of static seats will jeopardise the intended learning impact.

Within the UK higher education sector there are specialist groups that advise on equipment for teaching spaces, including audio, heating, lighting, induction loops, etc. Sadly, not all architects, builders and fit-out companies have the same necessary understanding of how buildings and technology should be integrated. Technology experts should be involved in a building project from the start. This can sometimes save a fortune in the form of unexpected costs to rectify sub-standard rooms. Multi-million-pound academic buildings have been opened with inadequate technological equipment simply because a proper consultation had not taken place. Another pitfall also needs to be avoided. Integrators make money by supplying and installing equipment for university clients. There is a danger that, if unchallenged, they will specify over-elaborate equipment which academic staff will find difficult to operate. Selected technology should be suitable for the task of enhancing learning.

Chapter 14

The LaTTE Project at the University of Wolverhampton

Duncan Peberdy

The Learning and Teaching Test Environment (LaTTE) project sought to transform an uninspiring window-less teaching space into an attractive facility that would help Wolverhampton University create future student-centred active learning spaces. Its development was based on consultation with a wide range of university stakeholders, including students. Where students previously experienced a soulless room in which staff were forced to transfer knowledge in front of rows and columns of single desks, they now enjoy an inspiring space which enables them to work in small active groups to create knowledge, supported by staff who can utilise the whole space.

Technology is key, but only to enhance learning. As soon as students enter the room, which is now decorated with bright vibrant colours, the furniture and layout are already telling them that they can expect and engaging experience. The group tables, each with an integrated display, are safe havens at which to work and students are provided with power for mobile devices, and chairs with mobility and comfort. They can quickly establish a small community which is engaged and ready to learn.

As well as the new décor and improved lighting, removing the gloom of the previous room (of course it's the same room – you just wouldn't recognise it), a new glazed door with a glass side-panel was installed. The university wanted people to see that something special was happening in this room. But the door also ensures that this creative space isn't being misused for traditional 'chalk 'n talk'.

Because the room features a system that transfers information between all of the tables and the main display, and which allows students to connect, use and share their own computing devices, it was important to ensure that the learning technology can be used intuitively. To eliminate any potential problems that would detract from learning, Wolverhampton employed learning technologists to support each session. Their presence allowed staff to teach without any fear of technology breakdown, and their observations identified scope for improvements.

Throughout the first year of operation (2012-13), the room was only made available to lecturers who had asked to teach there and who were using active learning methods with their students. Staff from five of the university's eight schools used the room with students, and it was also used for 'away days', meetings and 'showcase days'.

During the year, students and staff provided regular feedback on their experiences: 85% of students said the design of the room had a positive effect on group work and their learning, and 70% believed that their learning had improved. Staff feedback was overwhelmingly positive on all aspects: pedagogical methods could be used more effectively, support for students was improved, and the room generated heightened levels of debate and communication.

The LaTTE project has proved invaluable as a basis for developing a strategy to expand active learning methodologies across the university. Not everything has worked. For example, the teal-coloured glass writing boards require improvement, and students initially thought that the table-based screens were interactive. Even since the room opened, the world has witnessed advances in wireless technology that can be used to improve student use of their own devices in group learning scenarios. In due course Wolverhampton will introduce these into the LaTTE room and its wider active learning strategy.

The LaTTE project has been true to Wolverhampton University's motto: 'Innovation and Opportunity'. Two new buildings, furnished with the latest facilities, are due to open in 2105. So active learning has an exciting future at Wolverhampton.

Chapter 15

Using the LaTTE Room at the University of Wolverhampton

James Pearson-Jenkins

Senior Lecturer, Adult Acute Nursing and Academic Translation, School of Health and Wellbeing, University of Wolverhampton

In my role as an academic translator, I work with colleagues in our school to design learning objects that help students to improve their understanding of concepts. These are made available on our VLE for future use. I was therefore already working closely with learning technologists and the university's 'Blended Learning Unit' when I heard about the LaTTE project.

Although my own university learning was mostly a didactic experience, my understanding of anatomic physiology was based on first-hand familiarity, including the observation of surgeons in the operating theatre. My teaching has always sought to engage students before, during and after formal classes, so whilst the approach of teaching in the LaTTE room wasn't entirely new, the opportunity to discover the real benefits from being in such a space was not to be missed.

I was a little concerned that I received only minimal notice of access to the LaTTE room. A longer period for re-designing my lectures for group work would have been welcome. I recognise that some colleagues would have needed time for effectively re-designing PowerPoint-based lectures as active learning sessions. The big challenge is to make the new technology enhance learning without PowerPoint.

In my view, the LaTTE room is particularly suitable for problem-based learning because the tables automatically encourage joint working at problems, without the need for a chairperson. The sociality of small teams produces learning in which students share personal experiences, building a context which cannot be acquired by simply listening to knowledge or reading facts online.

There are good reasons why some teaching has changed; cost, health and safety, and cultural considerations. You couldn't, for example, dissect a cow's heart in a standard classroom. Yet the LaTTE room perfectly supports a wide range of learning through the use of technology. For example, students can investigate the structures and anatomy of a heart by manipulating three-dimensional images. Such resources build up knowledge and understanding far more than the two-dimensional drawings in books with their complex language.

The LaTTE room also challenges me to think more about my teaching. When students first arrive in the room they instantly recognise that their experience is going to be different, and assume that different means better. This makes me think constantly about how I can use the technology to strengthen engagement with students and improve learning. If they were not directed to work in groups and use their own technology they would be disappointed. The LaTTE room has definitely increased student engagement and grades have risen.

It has typically taken students 2-3 weeks to feel comfortable in the LaTTE room. They were previously accustomed to a situation in which use of mobile devices was discouraged. It took a while for them to be confident about using smartphones and tablets. One consequence of using the LaTTE room was that students didn't want return to 'normal' classrooms with rows and columns of desks. I don't know if this was an effect of the room itself or of the students' activity in it. Active learning doesn't work in traditional classrooms, so when using those 'traditional' rooms and methods afterwards I felt I was doing the students a disservice.

I have wondered if improvements could be made to the space and technology that would help learning. Visualisers are powerful tools and could be used more effectively. They are excellent for such tasks as teaching injection techniques as they clearly show the size and scale of different sized needles. It could also be useful to have a Twitter feed that ticker-tapes across the bottom of the individual displays to provide instant peer feedback. I would also like to have an experiment bench with a live camera so that students can observe what is taking place while they are sitting at group tables, and can collectively examine what is happening. I'm aware that sometimes students follow and imitate work at neighbouring tables. This could be prevented by having retractable dividers between the tables.

Finally, I'm concerned that as a profession, academics have no real impetus to strive for excellence in teaching. But as our motto is 'Innovation and opportunity', we have to live up that ideal. Facilities such as the LaTTE room are key to implementing Wolverhampton University's strategic vision and a great advert for attracting students from families without previous university attendance. They also discourage students from dropping out, thereby helping staff morale.

Innovations such as the LaTTE room are positive on so many levels.

Chapter 16

The 'Turn and Learn' Room at Aberystwyth University

Duncan Peberdy

The 'Turn and Learn' room at Aberystwyth university, designed by Nigel Thomas, builds on previous attempts to create the perfect space for both tutor-led instruction and team work. Development of the design took a year, and the room was installed in summer 2013 as part of a major refurbishment project.

Learning spaces have traditionally been designed in a particular format for a single purpose: as lecture theatres, seminar rooms, or specialist laboratories. Active learning involves a mixture of teaching and learning styles, so a variety of spaces are required. It is common to brief a large cohort of students and then send them off to work in small groups elsewhere. But when numerous students are all looking for space that supports group working, problems arise. Previous attempts to provide for two different requirements in a single space have resulted in designs that compromise at least one element, and often both.

Though students love active learning rooms, administrators and timetablers dislike the smaller numbers of students that such rooms typically accommodate. When standard furniture is sometimes used to create new layouts in rooms, it can be tempting to squeeze extra tables and seats to increase capacity; but this can prevent the learning outcomes originally intended, by restricting a tutor's movement and effectiveness.

Nigel's Thomas's ingenious Turn and Learn room design creates an environment fit for both tutor-led instruction and active team work. Working with David Biddle at TOP-TEC, he proposed the use of higher tables towards the back of the room, creating a raked effect on a flat floor and providing all students with good sightlines to the front.

Students sitting at the front of the larger tables can turn forward to a 350 mm deep work surface when it is necessary to face the tutor. When they need to work in groups, Students can turn round and join the main 800 mm deep table which accommodates six people. The comfy, fully adjustable task chairs have castors, whilst the tables are fixed to the floor to maintain the room's integrity and to ensure that a tutor can access all tables to support the students. The provision of space for a lecturer to visit each group is essential to the design's successful functionality.

The room's previous arrangement with rows and columns of single desks accommodated 136 students. This has been reduced by the new facility to 72. But the smaller numbers gain far more from active learning than from previous teaching. Moreover, 'traditional' rooms were often unused when were dispatched elsewhere to undertake projects in groups.

Feedback from both staff and students at Aberystwyth University shows that Nigel's

Turn and Learn room is a great success, and staff have already requested more of these spaces. Students can see as soon as they enter the room that their experience is going to be rewarding. Whilst tutors can still deliver sessions in lecture style, the existence of such innovative spaces will suggest to the outside world that Aberystwyth has high aspirations for its students.

Nigel Thomas is the Learning Spaces Design and Development Manager at Aberystwyth University, and in 2011 the recipient of a SCHOMS scholarship that enabled him to spend six weeks researching learning spaces in Australia working with Professor Peter Jamieson, University of Melbourne, a leading international figure in learning space design Nigel maintains an informative blog on learning spaces at www.learningteachingspaces.blogspot.co.uk

Photography Courtesy of Nigel Thomas

For more details on 'Turn and Learn' contact TOP-TEC

Chapter 17

A Dual-Function Room at Loughborough University

Caroline Pepper
Learning Space and Administration Manager, Loughborough University

In the Design School at Loughborough University, room 'LDS017' falls well short of being a fitting room name for a specially designed space which enhances the student experience. As part of the £22 million new-build project completed in 2011, Caroline Pepper worked collaboratively with the school and their architects, Burwell Deakins, to create a lecture experience unlike any other on the campus.

The prospect of a didactic lecture fills most students with dread. Standard lecture auditoria have remained largely unchanged for years. They have certainly not been up-graded to cope with active learning styles. Universities now understand that learning spaces must change to suit current learning methods by facilitating group work.

Loughborough University's Learning and Teaching Space Strategy is to, 'maximise the quality, flexibility and utilisation of all teaching space to effectively support the student experience', and as a result has focussed on the key principle; 'to encourage of students to learn by conversation not isolation'.

The Loughborough Design School briefed its architect to create a lecturing space that also facilitated group work. It is increasingly common for a large cohort to be given instruction for a short period of time and then to form groups for the rest of a session. An enormous amount of time can be wasted in searching for space to support dozens of small groups. That can also leave a lecture theatre standing empty, even though it was booked for the whole time.

The Design School concept was based on traditional Kabuki Japanese style theatre where audience is seated in groups in the central and peripheral areas and the performance takes place around the audience allowing them to feel more engaged. It was agreed that in designing this a student would feel more of a participant than an observer.

Within LDS017, Burwell Deakins have created a raked lecture theatre that arranges students in small groups. Switching from lecture mode to group collaborative working can happen instantly, providing more time for active learning by students. It is equipped for groups of four students to share a laptop or tablet screen, with wireless access to information.

The seating arrangement reduces the room's capacity by about 20 per cent, but the provision for group work without the need for additional spaces, plus the benefits to student learning counterbalance the reduced capacity. Loughborough University is planning similar dual-function rooms across campus and for Loughborough's new London Campus (on the Queen Elizabeth Olympic Park), and in Belfast, Queen's University has also implemented this design into their campus refurbishment.

There has been some very powerful feedback from staff at Loughborough about their use of their dual-function room. Opportunities provided by the room have challenged the way in which staff conduct their teaching. Surveys of students have shown they value the space for both formal teaching sessions and unsupervised group work. Early experience has taught Loughborough that future designs will require more space for circulation and better storage for coats and bags. But when students enter LDS017, they see a different kind of facility which creates an expectation that the learning and teaching they will experience will be of a very high quality.

Photographic images of Loughborough Design School
Courtesy of Hufton + Crow

Chapter 18

Modular Seating for Lecture Theatres

Nicholas Burwell

Burwell Deakins Architects

Lecture theatres have traditionally been used for the didactic delivery of instruction from one tutor to many students. But an innovative way has now been devised to construct from new or reconfigure lecture theatres for a mix of learning experiences.

The Burwell Deakins' 'Connect Seating' system was born from an understanding of contemporary pedagogy and the relationship between information-gathering and questioning which results in knowledge acquisition.

The company developed a modular arrangement for small groups for installation in a new auditorium at the Loughborough Design School. Through its geometry, each module provides an informal environment, and the auditorium can be used for traditional lecturing or group-focused activities without any need for rearrangement of either furniture or students. The initial designs were shaped by a broad range of influences, including both cabaret settings and Japanese kabuki theatre, whilst the form of the seating was inspired by the Giant's Causeway (Northern Ireland), where an informal landscape is created by repeating geometrical rock columns.

The initial design was developed in collaboration with Race Furniture to provide a set of three basic modules which can be organised for a wide range of auditoria footprints. The system has been successfully used for refurbishment projects at Queen's University, Belfast, and Exeter University.

The seating arrangement avoids the need for 'break-out space' and provides an excellent environment for informal learning. This reduces the total space requirements for teaching and collaborative active social learning whilst providing an asset that is likely to be in constant use. The design's simplicity and flexibility have proved extremely popular with users.

For information, contact: Nicholas Burwell, +44 (0) 208 305 6010

Images on following page of a Lecture Theatre refurbishment
at Queen's University, Belfast

Photography Courtesy of Marketing and Creative Services, Queen's University Belfast

PART 4
Technology for Active Learning Spaces

Chapter 19

WolfVision Visualisers
Duncan Peberdy

Theory is all well and good; but if 'seeing is believing', then the better we can 'see' the more effectively people will learn.

For a long time visualisers have been considered simply as slightly more sophisticated replacements for OHPs (overhead projectors). Instead of displaying an image, directly on to a wall, like an OHP, they are commonly connected to either a monitor or projector. They are often connected via a computer so that content can be captured and displayed in many different ways. Many manufacturers offer visualisers priced according to connectivity and features. It would be much better if such important aids to learning were valued instead for the quality of teaching they can inspire. Visualisers can help to engage and motivate students to achieve a much better understanding of academic and vocational subjects.

It is well recognised that learning spaces equipped with visualisers, enabling photos, documents and objects to be shown 'live' on-screen, create spontaneous interaction and participation. Being able to see displayed material in outstanding detail - including '3D' – helps students to understand difficult concepts more easily, and provides the opportunity to add real-life examples to theoretical teaching. The combination of a theoretical slide with a 'live' image on a second screen can be very powerful. Today 'student experience' greatly influences a choice of university, as is shown by the existence of pro-vice chancellors with responsibility for this aspect of universities. If it can be seen that a university or college has invested in the best learning technology, it is more likely to attract students.

Living on the Ceiling
WolfVision visualisers come into their own in situations where it is desirable to progress from theory to real-life experience. For example, veterinary students who have undertaken theoretical study can learn the nuances of clinical skills by watching an expert perform an anatomical procedure through a visualiser. Or consider a surgeon trying to teach many students but producing a scrum around his or her operating table, giving some students the best view but leaving others compromised. If there was a visualiser mounted from the ceiling

above the table, transmitting a live image back to a combination of large projection screen and multiple large displays every student would receive the best view. A visualiser can capture everything from an entire large animal down to the precise area in a small organ where an incision is required. Images can be frozen for students to discuss in small groups, and the whole procedure can be recorded as a video for the students to access again from their VLE (virtual learning environment).

The Centre for Comparative and Clinical Anatomy at Bristol University is using WolfVision ceiling visualisers in just the way described. Steve Gaze, the Centre's Teaching Services Manager, explains how WolfVision has advanced learning at Bristol. 'Anatomical specimens such as cadavers, skeletons and body parts are three-dimensional with deep holes and fissures, containing, for example, nerves, blood vessels and ligaments. With up to 120 students in a class, what is presented on the screen has to be seen clearly by all and provide an accurate, detailed representation of the specimens as the students need to understand and appreciate the 3D nature of objects as well as understanding the dissection procedures involved.' In this, Steve Gaze is referring to the depth of field and clarity achieved by the ceiling visualiser, assisted by its internal light. The light eliminates any shadows that might be caused by 3D structures while also illuminating the deepest recesses within the objects under examination.

A further advantage of visualisers mounted above desks is that they allow a table or lectern surface to remain free of equipment, putting nothing between a lecturer and his or her students.

The Beauty of Simplicity

An alternative to the ceiling visualiser is the WolfVision 'EYE' live-image camera. This is used, for example, at the Medway Campus of MidKent College in Gillingham. The college has six salons for training the next generation of hairdressers. Just as clinical skills are being learnt at Bristol, hairdressing techniques are being conveyed in Kent. Images from the camera are fed through a controller to a projector that displays a large image for an entire class. According to Teresa Daly, a lecturer in hair design 'All our students can now see close-ups of the detail involved in hairdressing techniques such as cutting,

Photography Courtesy of WolfVision

texturing, sectioning and colouring. Previously they had to crowd around a workstation with up to 17 students in each session. Many were not able to get a clear view of the demonstrations. With the cameras installed, their interest and input into the sessions have increased while the more confident can display their skills to show their fellow students what can be achieved. There is no doubt that the WolfVision systems have improved the quality of the training our students receive and their skills.' MidKent College also uses WolfVision EYE cameras to provide teaching to carpentry students.

Right On The Money

At Warwick University Business School a mixture of WolfVision's Ceiling Visualisers, EYE cameras, and more traditional visualisers are being used to enhance traditional teaching techniques in lecture theatres and classrooms. TOP-TEC's Voyager Lecterns have been modified with large 'dry-wipe' writing areas so lecturers can maintain eye contact with students while notes and explanations are made or student feedback is recorded. Traditionally these real-time annotations might have been made on a dry-erase board or flip chart, with the lecturer turning his or her back to the students to write. Using the combination of TOP-TEC lectern and WolfVision visualiser, the notes are projected on a class display for everyone to see more. This is clearer than a flip chart, and notes can be instantly captured and distributed directly to students or uploaded to the VLE.

In the Executive Centre lecture theatres at Warwick, a WolfVision ceiling visualiser is used to capture and display these real-time annotations. If the presenter walks away from the lectern, a large 'confidence monitor' behind the audience keeps the content in his or her view, so the lecturer doesn't have to return to the lectern to refer to the notes. At the lectern, a Synchronised Lightfield from the visualiser shows the lecturer the precise pick-up area of the camera, which adjusts in size when zooming in and out. So a presenter always knows exactly where to write or place objects. This greatly aids intuitive and effective use.

The visualiser equipment has proved so useful that in summer 2013 four teaching rooms were upgraded to provide the same functionality. The VZ-C12 ceiling-mounted model was unsuitable, so a combination of EYE Cameras and the VZ-3s Desktop Visualiser, mounted directly onto a TOP-TEC Voyager Lectern, were chosen instead.

TOP-TEC Voyager Lectern with WolfVision VZ-3s Visualiser
Photography Courtesy of Simon Collett, University of Warwick

More Than Just Pictures
WolfVision has now created the futuristic VZ-C6 Ceiling Visualiser, a model that features high definition video recording. It captures not only the WolfVision camera images but everything on the presenter's computer included in a presentation: PowerPoint slides, documents, photographs, webpages, etc. A line-level input is also provided which enables external audio sources to be connected to facilitate audio capture. In an age in which learning capture is increasing, it is advantageous for audiences and lecturers to have a single device that both captures everything and produces stunning image quality.

3D Pictures
WolfVision has also added the world's first stereoscopic 3D visualiser to its range, the VZ-C3D. This equipment will greatly enhance the accuracy and detail of learning applications when used in conjunction with a 3D-enabled display screen. It is especially suitable for the teaching of design, medicine, engineering and science more generally. People are now accustomed to 3D projection in which objects appear to be very close. The VZ-C3D features an adjustable depth control which allows a presenter to choose exactly how far the 3D image appears to be 'in front of' or 'behind' the 3D display.

Techno Booths
As classrooms and lecture theatres have ceased to be the only types of learning spaces, technology has allowed students equipped with tablet computers and smartphones to have access to media-rich learning resources – before, during and after formal instruction. Formal learning spaces on university and college campuses, together with existing technology, must

be adapted to deliver new ways of learning and support the devices now used by students.

At City University in London, a £2.3 million refurbishment of the university's library in Northampton Square included the provision of 'Techno Booths'. These are technology-equipped collaborative tables for students to continue active

learning outside formal tuition. Provision for such study is becoming increasingly common in universities. However, City's Techno Booths differ from other facilities by including a WolfVision EYE camera in the 'roof', so that almost anything on the table in the booth can be captured as a learning object and shared on the booth's screen. Since the refurbishment, the use of spaces for group collaborative study has risen by over 400 per cent.

Photograph Courtesy of Julien Bussell

Software is the New Hardware

Technology today delivers differences in outcomes through the quality and functionally of software. WolfVision now incorporates software with its products, supporting further advances in the improvement of teaching, and in learning and understanding by students. WolfVision's vSolution components also include software that allows mobile devices and PCs to interact directly with a WolfVision visualiser.

Photo courtesy of Weissengruber.biz

Active learning requires a lecturer to interact with different groups in a room. An object under the visualiser can now be annotated and manipulated (by zooming in or out) and captured using a tablet while a lecturer is with a group of students. The lecturer does not have to be within finger-touch of the visualiser. Students, in their groups, can use university-supplied equipment or increasingly, their own devices. Using wireless connection to a visualiser, they can in groups apply annotations to develop their learning, which can then be saved individually. Such increased student engagement with learning is exactly the kind of outcome that active learning seeks to achieve. It leads to greater understanding through building knowledge. It is yet another example of how 'Bring Your Own Device' methods, such as the use of iPads, are changing education. In this, software - vSolution - is the key.

Chapter 20

Sound Systems in Learning Spaces
Duncan Peberdy

Some visually stunning buildings have appeared on university campuses in recent times. They feature lots of glass walls, high ceilings in public spaces, tiled floors and open-plan areas. They are great on the eye, and great on the ear until people actually start to use such buildings, at which point noise pollution emerges from adjoining spaces. Why does this happen? Probably because as we can't see sound we either take it for granted or we don't realise the implications of creating environments using building materials that happen to perfect for generating echo and reverberation. The most likely explanation, however, is that the experts in audio visual matters at a university were not consulted until after a building had been constructed — by which time damage had been done.

Expectations that audio provision will be perfect in life have increased over recent years. It is now taken for granted that perfect audio is provided as standard. When was the last time you heard a television with poor sound quality? Video and audio conferencing have ceased to be bad experiences. And radio stations have been moving to digital frequencies that provide crystal-clear transmission. The quality of in-car audio has become superb.

Most home hi-fis and digital radios have controls for volume and probably also for balance. But professional audio systems in universities use digital processors that automatically configure the sound in many different ways. The equipment is designed to produce perfect audio throughout an auditorium. Current technical capabilities usually enable AV teams to offset architects' peculiarities of design, such as a room with one side wall at 90 degrees to the front and another at 60 degrees. Without the use of AV expertise and digital processing, the sound projection is such a room would be very poor.

Designing and Constructing for Auditory Excellence
Sound quality is essential for communication to be comprehensible. This principle is affirmed, for example, by the requirement of systems to enhance audio for people with impaired hearing. The provision of good audio, however, in new or refurbished buildings requires collaboration by stakeholders from the start. Allocating extra time up front provides the opportunity to create facilities that are good for teaching and minimise the need for technical support. Inadequate planning can easily cause errors and high additional costs.

The first aim of any educational building must be to create technology-enhanced spaces with outstanding facilities that advance learning - anything contrary to this is a dereliction of duty. Audio requirements should be included right from the outset in the architect's design work, ideally with advice from a specialist audio consultant.

Audio Considerations for Active Learning
The transmission of knowledge in a lecture theatre, typically using a 'goose-neck' microphone on a lectern, is very different from teaching in an active learning environment. In the former

situation, voice reinforcement is the key requirement, so that all students can hear, and also so that lectures can be captured and uploaded to a VLE for later access by students. But it is hard to use technology in a lecture theatre for questioning and interaction. Audience contributions can be difficult to hear and record. Solving this is difficult without causing students to 'switch off'. Either there have to be microphones that can be passed to audience members, or the tutor has to repeat the questions. Both can be time consuming.

Facilities designed for active learning are easier to support with audio equipment. They enable a tutor to circulate around a room and quickly get to any individual student. If Synergy tables are installed, each seating 5-6 students, it is feasible and cost-effective to provide a microphone at each table. In rooms designed to prompt conversation, every contribution must be heard clearly by the whole room and captured by the learning-capture system.

Wireless Flexibility

As in the development of personal computing, advances in audio have exploited wireless connectivity to provide mobility. Active learning spaces have been developed in which a tutor working with a small group can bring something to the attention of a much larger class via audio. Enabled with a wireless microphone, he or she can communicate instantly and clearly.

Wireless microphones were once prone to interference, especially from mobile phones, but Revolabs has solved this technological problem. The company's microphones are all impervious to GSM noise from other wireless electronic devices, which is important for efficient communication in teaching spaces.

Another consideration is the impact of the UK's 'Digital Switchover' in 2012, under which UHF wireless frequencies have been reallocated to new priorities, such as wireless broadband and high definition TV transmission. Revolabs wireless microphones avoid problems arising from the Digital Switchover because they use the DECT personal communication protocol instead, which is well outside the UHF spectrum. Without going into technical depths, all DECT phones operate within a certain frequency, but work without interference because the phones are individually 'paired' to the receiving base. All Revolabs microphones are securely encrypted and paired to their base unit so that if you speak in one room, the audio won't be heard in the next room erroneously.

Further Advantages of Revolabs Equipment

Revolabs microphones use rechargeable battery technology that typically takes two hours to charge and provide eight hours of continuous use. As soon as a microphone is removed from a charging unit it is automatically paired with a base station and ready to work. "One of the most useful features for the users and technical supporters is that the Revolabs microphones can be set to be active only once they're taken out of the charger units. There are no buttons to press – out of the charger is on, and back in is off. Simplified functionality for the users." Rob Hyde – AV Manager, University of Bath.

Revolabs microphones can also be added to existing infrastructures on a campus. Revolabs equipment incorporates standard features to provide security. These are included to meet stringent demands for military and corporate environments.

It is sensible on a campus to install equipment across the campus rather than just one or two expensive 'lighthouse' installations. This makes a larger contribution to students' learning, and Revolabs can provide a range of wireless microphones with different functionality, all of which are interchangeable. The adoption of a campus-wide policy is also sensible because only a one manufacturer is required for support; AV technicians only have to deal with a single product line and it helps lecturers and tutors to become familiar with the technology.

Chapter 21

Technical Considerations for Sound Systems

Rob Hyde
AV Manager, University of Bath

Users of teaching spaces have differing preferences in their approach to learning. Some like tactile learning, some auditory, some visual, and some a combination of audio and visual.

The 'normal' use of university teaching spaces combines audio and visual presentations and suits most students: a combination of image and sound sticks in the mind as a set of recallable scenes. This explains why people can remember lines from films and TV programmes.

The use of audio sources has become well established in education, through the creation of formal strategies and materials since the 1970s. More recently technical methods of delivery have changed, and some standards have improved. The quality of both sound production and output is of crucial importance. There is little point in having an expensive playback system if the source is awful. And if sound quality can be preserved from source to the reception end, there will be many options for post processing the signals. The move into digital forms of audio files has made some activities relatively easy, such as lecture capture and the creation of virtual learning environments. But it could be also argued, especially by audio purists, that we have actually lost the ability to 'hear' good quality audio. In practice we are probably working at a level determined by the capabilities of ordinary users. The newest digital compression formats and methods of delivery (especially immediacy of processing) mean that users can create materials relatively easily. The best way forward is probably a balance of audibility, consistency and operability. Technical services can support users by providing familiar types of equipment and ensuring reliability.

Many universities have moved from provision of teaching spaces for individual faculties to situations where all faculties share a centrally managed pool of rooms and equipment. Where this has happened, control mechanisms for equipment (the 'dashboard' of controls) must be identical so all users can work in any room. The use of general teaching also favours standardised equipment. Effectively, we're proposing homogeneity. Ideally there should be a minimum standard of equipment appropriate for users' requirements. If we assume that the functionality will include source playback (from PC, DVD/BluRay), lecture capture, voice reinforcement and hearing support, then equipment will require sophisticated audio processing to ensure that signals can be delivered not only for immediate sound, (i.e. to an audience) but for capture and hearing support.

To provide consistency requires separate treatment of large tiered theatres and the flat classrooms. The larger tiered theatres tend to require more complex equipment than smaller rooms to achieve a similar effect, but functionality for users is the same. The audio sources remain the same but inputs and amplifiers are different. It is interesting to note that most systems in university teaching rooms separate audio and visual signals so that they can be processed and controlled independently.

A typical audio system is represented by the diagram below, although in practice systems vary in scale according to the type of room involved.

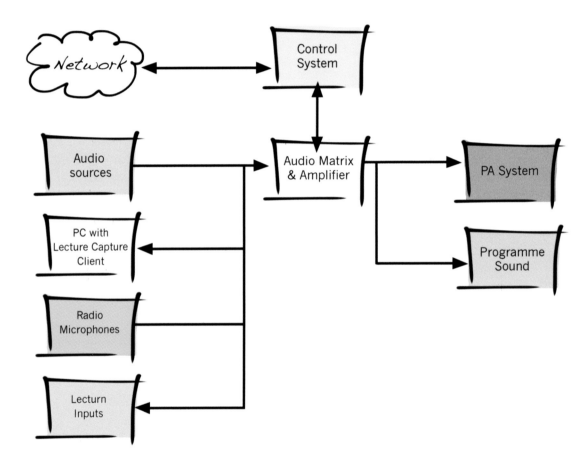

To achieve consistency across all rooms, system designers must engage in in-depth dialogues with users about teaching methods, and determine the requisite technical functionality. But minimum specifications for all rooms come at a price, and might be perceived as unnecessarily expensive. The gains would be rooms of uniform standard and familiarity for users.

One of the most interesting 'problems' in recent years has been the Ofcom's wireless spectrum microphone allocation. Where teaching spaces are in close proximity, the standardisation of audio equipment, and especially radio microphone voice reinforcement, is extremely important. In the case of Bath University, where there are 200 rooms with standard equipment, the standard bandwidth allocation has proved insufficient. The result is interference or even cross-reception. This can happen not only between adjoining rooms but between floors.

One of Bath University's most advanced buildings includes audio systems that provide full integration of: voice reinforcement, programme sounds, hearing support and lecture capture. Because signals enter and leave the systems, some degree of intelligent audio switching was needed in all rooms. Though this increased the cost it made the interface easier for users. The design was complicated but the interface for users relatively simple. There is a matrix in each room so that signals can be fed to functions as required, as well as being available for processing.

As the diagram on the opposite page shows, signals from the voice-reinforcement system need to be routed to both the lecture-capture system and the hearing-support system as well as to the PA system. In tiered theatres (with 300, 400 or 500 seats), this may mean transmission of radio microphone signals across 30, 40 or 50 metres or more, and the routing of signals around the theatre through longer signal pathways. Most rooms at Bath University use Revolabs HD-based microphone systems, which in turn use the DECT spectrum (1880 to 1900 MHz (DECT EU)). This avoids dependence on meeting one of the bandwidths available from Ofcom (at the time of writing DECT is license free). In high-density areas, the systems have settings enabling the spectrum to be split effectively into two ('A' and 'B' frequencies) and providing for manipulation of the transmission range. Where equipped rooms are adjacent and arranged in large blocks (not an infrequent occurrence in university buildings) this allows for alternating 'A' and 'B' rooms along corridors or on different floors. The units work by pairing each transmitter (in pairs) with its own receiver, and the transmission process is 128-bit encoded, which provides sufficient security. A useful feature of Revolabs microphones for users and technical supporters is that they can be set to become active only when removed from charger units. This happens automatically.

The Revolabs systems perform well in their situations, and can be expanded so long as the density of rooms is not too great. It is possible to ensure that individual buildings do not run out of DECT space.

Another important consideration is that audio systems in teaching spaces should remain functional even if the visual part of a system is not being used. This is for two reasons: first, some academic staff do not use AV facilities for each session, but will sometimes use just audio technology to facilitate debate; secondly it is essential that a hearing-support system is always active. The latter is normally achieved by using a standard gooseneck microphone on the lectern top in each room, from which sound is always relayed to the room PA and the hearing-support (loop) driver. The control system working in tandem with the audio side of the system allows for individual control of input and output levels.

Hearing support is often a neglected matter. For teaching rooms, this means hearing loops. They can be either physical tape loops or infra-red emitters (with a personalised loop).

When lecture-capture is used (as happens increasingly) audio signals have to be fed into a capture device. There is usually an external hardware unit or a built-in PC. In either case, signals have to be routed into the recorder. When a PC is used, capture devices for audio and visual signals are needed. This means that a PC can serve simultaneously as an audio source and recording device.

Though audio systems in teaching rooms are sometimes treated as an after-thought, they are fundamental to interaction between users. They deserve the same consideration as the clarity of visual images. Audio provides users with a fundamental link to their senses. They deserve the best possible quality of sound.

Revolabs HD-based Wireless Microphones

'Out of the charger is on, and back in is off'.

Chapter 22

The Crestron AirMedia™ Wireless Presentation Gateway

Duncan Peberdy

When people in olden days wanted to share information from a laptop through a large display screen or projector, they plugged in a VGA display cable, simultaneously pressed the Function and F5 keys and crossed their fingers. After a few seconds, the images on the laptop screen appeared on the big display, but then it was necessary to reconfigure something because the picture didn't have the same scale as the one on the laptop. When information was required from another laptop, the cable was unplugged and passed to someone else for the connection process to be repeated. Meanwhile, the audience waiting to see the information became bored and distracted. The introduction of HDMI cables simplified the process, but even HDMI cable-sharing has problems. For example, how do you connect an iPad or iPhone?

Crestron AirMedia is a wireless receiver which connects to a display screen to receive information from a laptop and duplicate it on screen. No wires are involved, no reconfiguration and no distractions.

It works in exactly the same way if you have a Mac, iPhone, iPad, Samsung Android, or almost any other device with a browser. Regardless of their devices, up to 32 people can wirelessly connect their devices to AirMedia and transition from one to another immediately, intuitively and effortlessly. If information has to be compared and contrasted, AirMedia provides a simultaneous viewing from up to 4 devices on a single screen.

A clever aspect of AirMedia is that it sits on a wireless network. An app on a personal device shows any AirMedia connection in range. When a person selects a preferred connection he or she is prompted to enter a four-digit PIN. The number automatically regenerates for each new session, and is shown in the top right corner of the display, meaning that people outside a room are unable to connect randomly.

If a person is on the network but not in the room, providing someone has provided the PIN number, he or she can connect and on their own screen view the information that is being shown in the room. This feature adds visual value to a telephone conference call or perhaps a remote tutorial.

If multiple AirMedia units are deployed around a campus, any configuration changes or software updates can be distributed to all units. Client software can be added to a standard build-configuration for Windows or Mac OS devices.

Crestron AirMedia:

No Wires

No Reconfiguration

No Distractions:

Just the information you want everyone to see, share and discuss.

CRESTRON CASE STUDY

Crestron AirMedia™ at William Jewell College

William Jewell College in Missouri, USA, is a top-ranked liberal arts college at which affordability and quality coexist. Students are taught to think independently, respect differences, connect ideas and challenge assumptions. These are some of the requirements for successful active learning.

In summer 2013 the new Pryor Learning Commons (PLC) was opened, providing students with a 24/7 facility for collaborative learning. Innovation has always featured strongly at William Jewell, and instead of books, the PLC facility features the latest in workspaces and technology to assist students in working collaboratively to create their own knowledge. Throughout planning and construction, academic staff and students were consulted extensively about the technology that would advance their studies. As a consequence the PLC contains a variety of rooms to support different styles of learning. The building was intentionally made as flexible as possible so as to see what kinds of positive results it could produce. The college provost, Dr. Anne Dema, wrote of the PLC, "We wanted a place that would be the intellectual centre of our campus, where students have access to information in an environment that encourages creativity, collaboration, and active learning."

In addition to social areas (with sofas, fireplaces, scenic views and coffee shops), the PLC contains a mix of classrooms and collaboration stations, facilitated with wireless equipment, in which students can immerse themselves to create knowledge together. To facilitate information-sharing in the class space and when groups are using collaboration tables, students can connect their wireless devices to Crestron AirMedia receivers, which display their information on screens.

In keeping with the working practices of the current young generation, tables had to provide enough space for five or six students to work collaboratively, and the information-sharing infrastructure had to support all kinds of wireless devices. After evaluating screen-sharing products, William Jewell College selected Creston AirMedia for security, connectivity, size and cost, and above all usability. AirMedia supports all devices, and enables the sharing of within small groups or in classes.

Up to 32 students can simultaneously connect to each AirMedia receiver, and their screens can show a single display or be divided into quarters and show up to four information

sources. The latter arrangement is perfect when one wants to compare information within a single screen.

 After the Pryor Learning Commons was opened, it was been heavily utilised by mobile-savvy students working together around the collaborative tables and instantly sharing information through the Crestron AirMedia wireless system.

Pryor Learning Commons at William Jewell College, Missouri, USA
Both photographs courtesy of
Joe Nickell/AV+Design

Chapter 23

NEC Engages Tablet Technology in the Classroom
NEC Display Solutions

Every young person possesses potential, which every teacher strives to unlock and nurture. But when classes are large, with say over 30 students, each with his or her own characteristics and complexities, it takes great skill, energy and enthusiasm for a teacher to engage with individual students. One answer is to embrace classroom technology. A variety of audio visual techniques have been shown to bring lessons to life and stimulate young minds, helping children to focus, engage and retain knowledge.

Collaborative Learning with DisplayNote
In cooperation with DisplayNote, NEC Display Solutions offers interactive classroom technology that involves every member of a class and encourages active participation. It can be easy for a reluctant or reticent student to hide at the back of a class, making no trouble for the teacher, but there is a good chance he or she will disengage. Through collaborative learning techniques, DisplayNote actively promotes engagement, offering opportunities for even the most timid student to strive to fulfil his or her potential.

Complementing the trend towards tablet-based classroom solutions, DisplayNote software enables the screen of any connected device to be annotated and shared with any other connected device - the perfect arrangement for BYOD (Bring Your Own Device) initiatives. In universities, students are keen to use their own smart devices, and BYOD collaborative techniques are increasingly used in small-group learning areas using DisplayNote to connect to a large-format display.

Empowered to take Ownership
Using DisplayNote, the screen of any connected device can be shared with any other connected device. Tablets, PCs, laptops and smartphones, projectors, whiteboards and touch screens can all be networked via a WLAN (wireless local area network) router to a teacher's PC. The software works via a uniform interface linked to all such devices, enabling students to receive, link to and save teaching material and add their own notes. A student can also become a presenter, with his or her own work appearing on a projected whiteboard image. Through collaborative working, all students are empowered to take ownership of class discussion and are actively encouraged to participate through using a highly intuitive device.

DisplayNote also allows a teacher to control all connected devices, including the projector, without having to use a remote control, which can easily be mislaid in an educational environment. By controlling from a wireless Tablet device, a teacher can move freely round a class, and is not restricted to leading from the front.

Since the late 20th century, NEC has influenced the development of technology in education, and its projectors and desktop and public displays have become a central part of lessons, lectures and information distribution in many educational facilities across Europe. NEC technology adds life, reality and interactivity to the curriculum, and also familiarises students with the kinds of technology they will use in later life.

Chapter 24

NEC and DisplayNote

Ed Morgan
Head of Marketing, DisplayNote Technologies Ltd.

DisplayNote is a computer application designed for student-centred learning environments, and for environments in which teamwork, collaboration and communication are integral. It provides a practical response to three questions that are often asked when organisations develop active learning spaces:

1.	How do we best highlight student learning rather than an instructor's teaching?
2.	How do we make the best use of space?
3.	How do we convert existing lectures to different meaningful activities?

Before examining DisplayNotes's role in answering these questions, it is important to understand its characteristics and features. DisplayNote is cross-platform, device-agnostic collaboration solution designed to let presenters control their computer using a tablet device or phone, to transmit content from that computer to multiple devices, and to allow other participants to collaborate in real time and contribute to a presentation using their own mobile device. Participants in a DisplayNote session or lesson can capture a presenter's content on their own device, personalise it by adding their own notes, and save everything on their device either to review or export. Sessions can take place either over a local area network or over the 'cloud', meaning that students can join lessons remotely. DisplayNote also allows teachers to connect their laptop to a projector via wireless connectivity, and to control their projector with a mobile device.

Highlighting Student Learning Rather than an Instructor's Teaching

The essential function of DisplayNote is to take activity on a presenter's screen and share it with a student's device. It therefore transfers attention from teacher to student and enables each student to focus more on his or her screen that on the teacher's display. The collaborative nature of DisplayNote allows instructors to select students to work together on content shown on the main display and to interact with that content using their own mobile devices.

In a traditional learning space an instructor stands at the front and works from a whiteboard or projector, delivering a lesson to a group of students all arranged in theatre-style seating with their focus on the front. When this scenario is advanced, in regards to technology with an interactive whiteboard or projector or touch display placed at the instructor's disposal, the lesson now becomes interactive though students continue to sit in theatre-style seating focusing on the front. Both of these scenarios, by their nature, highlight the instructor's teaching rather than the student's learning. Even in the advanced scenario, interaction comes primarily from the instructor.

The collaborative nature of DisplayNote software allows an instructor to change teaching and learning in two ways: first, students can contribute to a lesson or presentation using a mobile device, secondly, students can use mobile devices to work together. For example, consider the rudimentary example of an instructor displaying a world map and teaching students about continents. In a traditional lesson, an instructor provided a spoken outline of knowledge about continents. Students listened, made notes and used their notes for review. Using DisplayNote, an instructor can transmit a world map to each student's device and ask students to contribute by drawing on screen and sharing their drawings with the class. If a student is, for example, asked to locate Africa, he or she can use DisplayNote to annotate the map and share it. The result is individualised learning.

Another possible teaching scenario involves dividing a class into small groups and, using DisplayNote in collaborative mode, asking those groups to contribute to a presentation in a similar way. In this instance, class time is given to collaborative work by students. When an individual or group reaches a solution, it can now be easily shared with others.

Making Best Use of Space

It is natural, given human dynamics, for students to look instinctively towards a teacher; and a combination of voice, visuals and pointing is a powerful way of drawing attention to information.   But pedagogical models are changing toward lessons that facilitate interaction between teams of students engaged on short, interesting tasks. While they work their instructor is free to roam around asking questions, asking one team to help another, or asking why answers have differed. Lessons, more so than ever, are class-wide discussions with many opportunities to interact.

Incorporating technology such as DisplayNote gives a tutor the option to work just at a board or transfer a main display to mobile devices. Now he or she can roam around the room, engage with individuals or groups and, at the same time, present wirelessly from an ipad, control a computer and/or projector remotely, or send images and drawings from their device to the main display. In addition, DisplayNote technology offers room designers the freedom to consider almost any type of design, knowing that a main instructor can be positioned anywhere.

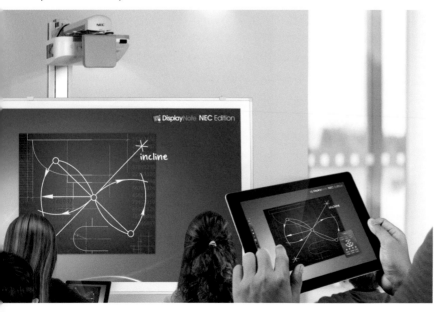

Converting Lectures to Meaningful Activities

An important challenge in the introduction of active learning environments is the conversion of existing types of lectures to new meaningful activities. This requires instructors to undertake training in the use of visual and audio tools. DisplayNote seeks to expedite this process. Because DisplayNote transmits material from an instructor's screen, he or she can use existing resources, lesson plans, and course materials alongside new equipment such as tablet devices and smartphones without the need to reformat, republish or recreate content.

DisplayNote also provides for instructors to test the understanding of students quickly and discretely. This is achieved via the software's student polling feature which allows instructors to pose questions to and receive replies from a student's device. Often employed by teachers at the beginning of a lesson, it is a useful way for instructors to avoid giving time to reconsidering basics and devote class time to the more difficult aspects of the material in hand. If used during a lesson, this feature can find gaps in understanding and facilitate lesson modification.

Conclusions

With research showing that active learning environments are more expensive to create than standard teaching rooms, DisplayNote seeks to enhance existing equipment such as mobile devices, touch displays and interactive projectors or whiteboards. In addition to improving classroom teaching, DisplayNote enables students to join lessons from off-site locations, thereby promoting active learning by students campus-wide.

Tidebreak Case Study

Teaching for the 21st Century at Winona State University

Founded in 1858, Winona State University (WSU) in the USA is a comprehensive public university with about 8,800 students. The oldest member of the Minnesota State Colleges and Universities System, Winona State offers 80 undergraduate, pre-professional, licensure, graduate, and doctorate programs on its three campuses: the original Main Campus in Winona, the West Campus in Winona, and Winona State University-Rochester.

Teaching and Technology

As with many educational institutions throughout the USA, the Winona State University student body has grown up using many forms of technology in their everyday lives. Students usually arrive on campus having used computers, laptops, mobile phones and tablets for many years and are considered technology-savvy by today's standards. Just as in the business community, where the BYOD (Bring You Own Device) phenomenon has taken root, students now come to universities having used technology for many years and expect facilities to include modern technology.

Yet while technology continues to evolve, many students find that universities are not at the forefront of technology use and cannot afford to spend large sums of money on new forms of technology. At the same time, many faculty members and IT leaders see the benefits of incorporating new forms of technology into the classroom setting. For WSU, adopting new forms of technology is seen as essential for growth. Ken Geaetz, WSU's director of Teaching, Learning and Technology Services has observed: 'At Winona State University we feel very strongly that technology can help transform the educational experience and help prepare our students for life after graduation. Each student is given a laptop and tablet when they enroll because we feel it helps improve the learning process. Fortunately, our faculty members understand the benefits of having technology in the classroom.'

Evolution of Education

Ken Graetz is a technology enthusiast and is always on the lookout for new forms of technology that can help to improve student performance. In looking closely at the IT infrastructure at WSU, he realised that a shift was occurring within the university which was changing the landscape for the faculty. 'There's been a shift in the classroom at WSU over the past few years which involves flip learning', said Graetz. "In many cases students can go online to watch video of their professors lecturing, and what used to be considered homework is now done in class with the faculty member offering more personalized guidance and interaction with students. With so much classroom content available online, we began to see changes in the way faculty members led their classes. We asked ourselves. "How can we improve the classroom environment" and "How can we set things up so that students will work together and be more collaborative?"'

While there was no 'ah-ha' moment that instigated change, Ken Graetz began exploring different technologies that could change the way in which faculty members presented information to their students, and alter the methods by which the students worked with and mastered the course content. Fortunately, Graetz had seen technology from Tidebreak™ ten years earlier and realised that this could help address WSU's needs. 'What is important to understand is that we had a vision of improving the way faculty could work with the student body', said Graetz. 'The idea was to develop a system where faculty could come out from behind the podium and work hands-on with the students. At the same time, we wanted to create an environment where the students could work in small teams to attack problems in a group setting rather than as individuals. We wanted to incorporate technology that could enhance our investment in laptops and tablets.'

From Lecture to Active Engagement

While the BYOD movement brought technology-savvy students to WSU, faculty members and facilities lagged behind. The university was built in 1858 and its classrooms were designed for the traditional podium at the front of the room with faculty lecturing to students. In addition, the classrooms were not designed for today's high-tech world which meant that proper wiring and Ethernet capabilities were limited. And as with most academic environments, funds for making these types of technology upgrades were limited.

Fortunately, Ken Graetz and the IT team found a partner in Tidebreak that offered technology to create a collaborative learning environment at a cost-effective price. Starting with one classroom, WSU installed ClassSpotPBL™ software which is designed to combine interactive capabilities with small-team collaboration. It allows students and faculty to move effortlessly between 'teaching' and 'teaming.'

For example, students in a photojournalism class might be working on a project that requires input from the five members of a team. Each of their laptops is automatically connected to one monitor so the team can view multiple photos at the same time. In the past this was usually done by requiring all five students to look at the team leader's laptop. Students can now post photos to the group's monitor, move images around, mix-and-match photos from each student, and do all of this wirelessly and in real time. Almost immediately students can begin working together, share insights with their class on the main monitor, and be supported by a faculty member actively who is working with the small groups instead of lecturing from the front of the room.

What were the consequences of introducing the new software, for students and faculty? 'In my twenty years as a teacher this is the most significant change I've seen. I'll never teach the old way again,' said Ken Graetz. "Students used to sit back in their desks and wait for the teacher to lecture and, with any luck, stay awake during class. Now we have an environment where students and teachers actively work together to solve problems and master the curriculum. The students are much more engaged in the learning process, and the faculty members are now more like guides who help students master the material. ClassSpot is altering the way the faculty members lead their classes to take advantage of the new interactive environment.'

One of the benefits of implementing change at classroom-level is that reactions spread quickly. Students who use the Tidebreak-equipped classroom have constantly tried to obtain additional class time to take advantage of ClassSpot PBL. As Graetz commented: 'That classroom is booked 100 per cent of the time. We're trying to figure out how to adjust the schedule so that the room is available more often, which is a good problem to have.' Fortunately for the faculty, ClassSpot PBL was designed to help support all faculty members and students regardless of their capability with technology. 'It's easy to use and easy to deploy which is very important in our university,' said Graetz. 'It's very intuitive to use which means that training our staff is quick and easy. There's not a lot of wires and configuration needed and it runs on our existing network. But what I find most amazing is that we've redesigned how classes are being taught and it didn't take a monumental overhaul of the university's infrastructure or faculty to accomplish this change.'

Other campus leaders, including deans and department leaders, have observed ClassSpot PBL in action and see it as a way to change the teaching process and give students a competitive advantage when they graduate.

'Seeing how ClassSpot PBL has had such a positive impact on our university, I'd like to expand beyond the classroom to more informal settings, like the student union or the library', said Graetz. 'Using ClassSpot PBL has changed the way our faculty members teach, improved the way that our students learn, and opened us up to a world of possibilities since it's so easy to use and cost-effective. As an educator, I find it fascinating to watch how enthusiastic the students are to come to class.'

Tidebreak's ClassSpot PBL in action at Winona State University
Photo courtesy of Winona State University

PART 5
Installing Learning Spaces

Chapter 26

Planning Audio Visual Installations: An Overview

Roland Dreesden
Managing Director, Reflex Ltd

Since the early 21st century, Reflex Ltd has been involved, as an AV Integrator, in a revolution in the use of teaching and learning spaces, mainly affecting classrooms and seminar rooms. It has been driven, in part, by students themselves. Because secondary schools have embraced interactive learning, group study and collaboration, entrants to university expect to have continuing access to this type of environment. Universities have been required to create appropriate learning spaces.

Another influential factor has been the increasing connectivity of devices. Back around 2008 students and lecturers could only connect laptop PCs to projectors. By 2014 various devices - laptops, tablets, smart phones etc. - can be connected to presentation equipment in a learning space. Universities also became concerned to maximise the use of space; a limited and expensive resource. Multi-functional meeting and learning spaces became appealing assets.

These considerations have caused a dramatic shift in how universities engage with students. Traditional ways of teaching are being replaced with more relaxed, team-based, collaborative approaches. Students have begun to work in small groups and use their own devices for research and presentation. Students have been encouraged to carry out research even during lectures.

Reflex Ltd has been involved with several universities in the development flexible learning spaces. Whilst there is no prescribed formula for their appearance, a similar approach to design was adopted at each site. One installation completed in 2013 provides a good example.

The university concerned wanted to develop a collaborative teaching space that could be replicated on several constituent campuses, following rigorous testing by students and teachers. The starting point was a standard 40-student classroom-style room with a teaching desk at the front and rows of seating. It was equipped with 'standard' classroom audio visual facilities; a ceiling-mounted projector, front projection screen and basic connectivity for a classroom PC and a laptop. The space was then fundamentally 'upgraded'. It included a mobile teaching podium that can be used in various positions, including the middle of the room and anywhere across the front. The rows of seating were replaced by six 'petal' tables, each seating up to eight students. These allow group working and have local connectivity for transmission from tablets, laptops and other devices onto a large LCD display. Two high-definition projectors at the front enable teaching resources to be displayed. A lecturer can

select output from any of the petal tables, enabling students to share their work with the whole class through the front projectors. Students and teachers who have used the space have reported positively on their experiences.

Increasing Interactivity and Collaboration
The rapid development of 'touch' tablets implies that university education will soon involve intense interactivity. Interactive screens have already become widely used in small classrooms and learning pods, though not in large lecture theatres. The 'collaboration' and active sharing of information that is already familiar in the corporate world is likely to be adopted in HE.

Collaboration itself is nothing new. Video conferencing technology has been used for many years to enable people to communicate between offices in different locations. It is an obvious next stage for people to share information simultaneously in the same meeting room. It entails people sharing a screen display, either individually in sequence, or simultaneously. A key consideration is making the activity simple for users. This could be achieved by local wireless communication or via the university network. The type of computer employed requires consideration: a laptop, tablet or mobile phone? If it's a 'BYOD' (Bring Your Own Device) then legal and security elements have to be considered.

Recording and Distance Learning

Another technology-based growth area within higher education is lecture or presentation capture. There are five main reasons for this development.

The first is improvement of comprehension. Students may not absorb everything during a lecture or grasp a concept the first time round. Providing a means for re-watching a lecture and re-viewing the presentation material, helps to make the most of lectures. The second reason is increasing access to teachers. If lectures are available as recordings, a lecturer can instead provide time for direct engagement with students.

A third reason is the popularity of peer review. Recording student presentations allows other students to review and possibly to annotate their content. A fourth reason is improved access to teaching. Students learn in a variety of ways. Recorded lectures permit access at any time and through a range of devices. Students can work at their own pace, pausing and rewinding as required while working on a problem. A final reason is academic development. Recording lectures and presentation material allows teaching staff to review their performance. This helps to develop their teaching skills as also permits review by other academics. The introduction of lecture capture provides new challenges for systems integrators. If they are involved in planning a system from an early stage, capture can be designed in.

When AV systems are designed, the integrator must consider several important aspects. The first is audio or sound reproduction. Its importance in the improvement of teaching is often overlooked, and it becomes of paramount importance when considering lecture capture. There is difficulty in effectively capturing sound when a lecturer is moving around. Wireless microphones partially solve the problem but are not always reliable. But installed microphones can capture not only a lecturer but the audience, ensuring that collaboration and student participation are also recorded.

The choice and positioning of cameras are equally important, because it is essential that a moving lecturer is recorded visually.

It can be expensive to provide facilities for recording lectures. It is therefore important that any installation of technology is embraced by teaching staff to ensure a good return on investment. One of the best ways to achieve this is to ensure that the technology is simple and intuitive for users, especially the methods for starting and stopping recording. A university must also consider how and where recordings are to be stored and managed.

Early Engagement with AV Integrators

The planning and installation of AV technologies presents challenges for both clients and AV integrators. It is most important that an integrator should be able to engage with locations as early as possible. Integrators possess valuable knowledge of what is achievable, which is particularly useful when a new venture may be the first one undertaken by a university. It is likely that an integrator previously worked with other clients on developing similar spaces and can draw on this experience.

A university must also identify how users will connect to technologies, and how equipment will connect to their IT network. Another necessary early consideration is furniture: should it be off-the-shelf or custom-made? 'Desking' must not only hold and store the 'engine' of an AV system, but also be usable with students' devices. It may also need to be flexible such that space can be re-configured easily.

It is also important to consider the impact of AV technology within a space. This includes ensuring that the physical structure of walls, ceilings and floors are designed to accommodate equipment. Power and containment requirements have to be incorporated into a project design along with lighting and acoustics. This should be done at an early stage because problems can generate expensive costs if they occur at a late point.

Whilst the list of considerations for an AV project may appear daunting, Reflex Ltd, as an AV integrator, deals with such challenges on a daily basis. As long as the company is engaged at the earliest opportunity, and good communication lines are established, then the experience of project collaboration will work in everyone's favour.

Chapter 27

The Tendering Process with Educational Institutions

Nick Fitzpatrick
Director of AV, Universal AV

This article seeks to provide an insight into how systems integrators can encourage a move towards active learning strategies in place of traditionally presented seminars and lectures. This progression aims to support the integration of BYOD (Bring Your Own Device) and result in increased utilisation of space.

In practice, integrators tend to face difficult starting situations. Numerous new-build or refurbishment projects presented to integrators are flawed from the beginning. The education sector obsesses about price but fails to measure quality and value for money. Large projects are often encouraged to attract heavy discounts. If projects are to be successful there has to be a collaborative approach in which universities, manufacturers and integrators seek to understand collectively what it takes to deliver high-quality intuitive solutions.

However the biggest problem issue that AV (audio visual) integrators face is want of time. From the inception to the handover of projects insufficient time is usually allocated to generate new learning strategies and innovations. This becomes a challenge particularly for AV integrators because they are often the last trade to be involved. Universal AV has tried to be a proactive company with good management and planning. It has endeavoured to work with customers on innovations that will enhance teaching facilities. But too often the officers of institutions provide inadequate scope for high-quality planning.

After tenders have been issued, every element of the subsequent process often becomes rushed. Rooms are often unavailable for surveying. Infrastructure has often not been provided for. Specifications are vague. The budget has not been allocated correctly. The time for tendering is minimal. The usual result is that a company is appointed and spends valuable project time revising the specifications which were excessive for the budget. Sometimes utilities have been omitted, so the project is already on the back foot.

The Tendering Process: Current Inadequacies Case Study

The reality of the tendering process is exemplified by a case that had a total budget of £200,000 and the following timetable:

- 30 October: tender documents released.
- 4 November: site briefing
- 11 November: tender submission
- 10 January: project completion and handover

There were just ten weeks from start to finish. The tender was to be evaluated on the following criteria:

Criteria	Weighting
Agreement pricing	40%
Project management	20%
Post-sales support	15%
Contract management	10%
Administration	5%
Sustainability	5%
Marketing and promotion	5%
Total:	**100%**

After receiving the tender document from a university, on 4 November representatives of Universal AV were 'shoe horned' along with their competitors into a small meeting room, presented with a loose specification, and shown plans that proved to be several revisions behind the actual plans. It was agreed that the new tender submission date would postponed to 13 December, but the completion and handover date was not put back.

On 18 November Universal AV was informed that it was the preferred bidder because the purchaser was confident that it would somehow meet the completion date. It was unclear whether or not the bid had been assessed against the evaluation criteria. Representatives were asked to attend a meeting on 21 November to discuss the specification, which needed to be 'tweaked', and a full project meeting on 22 November. At the latter meeting the main contractor wanted to see a detailed specification and project plan. So far Universal AV had not been allowed to survey the site, view current plans, or receive an official purchase order. Eventually a site visit was scheduled for 25th November for undertaking a detailed survey. This proved crucial because it turned out that the purchaser's specification was unfeasible: little provision had been made for an audio visual installation.

By 29 November Universal AV's project team finalised a compromise specification which was very different from the original specification and vision. The project's scale was reduced to meet the installation timetable and lack of provision for AV. The company had now received an official order, but had just five weeks to organise and complete a project that had apparently been in planning for over three years.

Universal AV has always attempted to provide innovative, future-proof solutions for projects, but has found itself regularly compromised by factors created by institutional administrations. Though administrations often concede changes, they rarely alter the completion and handover date. This example of project planning is not exceptional, but typical. Institutions seem to think that project teams have empty desks waiting for the next big project to arrive. This is emphatically not the case.

How Can Projects Be Improved?

Informal discussions between universities, manufacturers and integrators have revealed that the internal processes for project approval lie deep within universities. What often appears to be a last-minute approach is often the result of budget uncertainty, or sometimes a lack of understanding of a school's requirements for rooms by people who control central timetabling. Unfortunately such uncertainties cascade down the management chain. As a result Universal AV's instinct to innovate and add value is compromised by budget and timescales. As an organisation it would like to be involved in a project as early as possible. Sometimes institutions claim that 'we didn't want to trouble you' just in case a project failed to materialise. Universal AV would prefer its team to follow the account management process; to discuss requirements, survey site or plans; to be able to demonstrate the latest innovations; and to provide a budgetary quote. If a project should not be implemented, a new relationship might at least have been inaugurated or and existing one strengthened. Far more projects come to fruition than are shelved. So involvement from the earliest opportunity would normally be advantageous for all concerned? It would enable a university, irrespective of its budget, to think about how AV can be built into the fabric of a new or refurbished building, how power and networks can be allocated, how walls might be strengthened, and to identify mounting points. Any time given to researching technology and innovation will provide a vision of possibilities and, more importantly, the extent to which they can be achieved.

The provision of an initial quote can make an enormous contribution to a project in two ways. It indicates how much must be spent to deliver innovation and a quality experience for fee-paying students. Secondly, it avoids the surprise caused when a last-minute tender produces responses over budget. This always results in changes to specifications and loss of valuable planning time. If an initial budget has to be reduced, the early involvement by a company means that an informed decision can be made about specification changes. Alternatively a high-quality solution can be achieved over a longer period because infrastructure can be created allowing for subsequent expansion of a facility. But if necessary quality can be compromised to stretch a budget. Effective early planning can also result in a project plan involving complete provision for AV and a project timetable that can be included in the main contractor's project.

When Universal AV has been selected as the preferred supplier, and before a purchase order has been issued, we recommend that a project meeting is held to finalise details, to appoint a project manager, and to ensure that clear lines of communication have been established. It is vital that both parties fully understand the project content and the collaboration necessary to achieve successful implementation. Depending upon the project's size, Universal AV recommends a minimum of six weeks' planning before work begins on site. Equipment has to be purchased, often including bespoke furniture which can require a month to procure; labour has to be allocated and project paperwork produced to ensure that the company's team is fully briefed. It is also necessary that the customer concurs with the company's plans. Above all, health and safety have to be ensured for everyone involved.

Conclusions

Universal AV is grateful for the project opportunities it receives, and always seeks to exceed expectation. But there has to a collaborative approach to projects. It is necessary for universities to understand the process required for a quality project to be delivered on time and budget. So often institutions neglect their responsibilities and projects are completed at the integrators' expense.

Institutions and companies must work in partnership to take advantage of great innovations, and to encourage active learning strategies focused on the improvement of education.

Chapter 28

Snelling BUSINESS SYSTEMS

Procurement: How to Avoid 'Summer Madness'

Toby Wise

Managing Director, Snelling Business Systems

In 2012 – 2013 over £22 million was spent by universities in the southern UK on audio visual systems under purchasing frameworks which provided access to pre-approved preferred contractors. Yet despite the existence of this structure, there are challenges within the ordering and supply system. With clients outnumbering contractors by almost 10 to 1, the normal requirement for systems to be installed in recess periods creates enormous pressure.

This is exacerbated by the complexity of the systems themselves. They commonly require bespoke software, and their deployment coordination with a client's IT team, estates department and other stakeholders. Hardware also has to be ordered at least 6 – 8 weeks in advance.

Such factors are troublesome enough, but many installations are bedevilled with additional troubles. The late arrival of purchase orders can lead to a last-minute rush for materials. Supply chains can prove inadequate for meeting demand. Sometimes equipment arrives a damaged or faulty condition. Such difficulties and a restrictive timescale impede or even prevent off-site preparation and on-site testing. Clients can experience late delivery, defective equipment, poor integration of equipment with their IT infrastructures, and in the worst cases disruption to teaching delivery. Failure with learning spaces can damage the reputation of systems suppliers and of university departments.

Current university purchasing policy partly creates and partly increases the difficulties, notably with regard to timescales and cash-flow. The date for budget confirmation, 1 August, coincides with the beginning of the main recess period when systems have to be installed. Given the limited number of pre-approved suppliers, and their limited resources, it is often necessary for a university client to outline its requirements to a supplier before it can place a purchase order. This then creates a 'Catch 22' scenario for the supplier: it can place its own orders with manufacturers, particularly for long-lead-time items (e.g. customised furniture) to ensure delivery, but in so doing it places itself in a dangerous situation. Or it delays ordering and risks unreliable delivery and substandard service but without risk, for example, to capital or cash flow.

Such scenarios can be illustrated in more detail by taking the example of the installation of several seminar rooms and lecture spaces. To achieve installation in summer requires the supplier to order equipment in May for delivery in late June, allowing time for off-site construction and testing in July. The supplier also needs time to deal with any faulty or damaged goods. Following this timeline provides reliable delivery for the client, but involves the following concerns for the supplier:

1. No purchase order against which to secure product procurement.
2. Restricted cash-flow, without stage payments; so monies expended in June will not be collected until project completion (typically September for invoicing, payment in October or November).

These difficulties make the framework-based education business less attractive than other commercial work for some suppliers.

Improving Project Delivery

In the increasingly competitive and commercialised world of higher and further education, UK institutions seek to provide excellent, state-of-the-art facilities for their academics and students. This is best achieved through carefully planned projects, with estates, IT and other stakeholders working in partnership with contractors and suppliers.

In turn, it is every supplier's goal to achieve a high-quality delivery of systems and services, exceeding a client's objectives and requirements and thus ensuring the possibility of repeat business. It is equally important, however, for the supplier to realise a commercial margin on products and services and minimise the risk to its capital.

Bearing in mind the problems discussed above, there are some practicable measures that could improve the ordering process for both parties, given that university budget confirmation dates are unlikely to change.

Vesting Certificates

The introduction of vesting certificates would allow suppliers to procure materials, and be paid for them in advance of on-site installation. This has the advantage to clients of guaranteeing high-quality, co-ordinated supply, whilst making framework-based education business more attractive to suppliers. Vesting certificates are commonly used in the construction industry, particularly when bespoke or scarce materials are involved, and when projects have restricted delivery windows. Given the financial stability of vetted framework suppliers, there would be minimal risk to clients in employing this approach.

Split Procurement

Use of a vesting certificate process would allow hardware to be procured before budget confirmation on 1 August. Labour, including installation, software and all 'soft' costs, could be settled after the August award. Such an approach would depend on a client organisation being able to raise a purchase order for at least the hardware element of its project ahead of on-site delivery.

Conclusions

Snelling Business Systems has always believed that working in partnership with universities and higher education organisations generates the most effective results. Addressing the general organisation of framework-based education business elevates this to a national level. Snelling would like to see all clients and suppliers routinely working in a collegiate way, meeting regularly to ensure good understanding of proposed projects and planning for the resources involved.   However, the real key to improving the 'summer madness' lies in the thorny issue of procurement arrangements and rescheduling the normal planning and purchasing cycle.

PART 6
Student's Experiences of Learning Spaces

Cardiff University

Geraint Davies (Mechanical Engineering, graduated 2012)

The buildings of Cardiff University are distributed throughout the city centre, with most departments possessing their own building. Because Engineering is a large department and the subject requires expensive high-spec computers and dedicated software, special password-protected areas were provided for students within the Engineering building. This proved valuable during revision and group sessions because the resources needed by students were always available, and the Engineering library was well kept and silent, with bookable conference rooms for group meetings.

During my time at Cardiff, an open-plan seating area was created in the Engineering building called 'The Forum'. It was a flexible learning space with a mixture of individual spaces with high-spec computers and group tables accommodating 6-8 students, with comfy armchairs and coffee tables in the middle.

During each semester we received 30+ hours of lectures, and then usually spent 2-3 weeks on revision and examinations. Each department had a different attitude towards revision, with some allowing access to past papers and providing tuition. My revision, especially in the third year, involved sitting at a table in the Forum with my 'tablet' computer and close friends from the course. We then went over past papers together and overcame problems through discussion and investigation.

Successful revision was based not simply on a single zone, such as The Forum, but on the Engineering Department on a whole. I could go to the University at 8 a.m. and find a relatively quiet area with all the required technology and also space for collaboration with other students. Everyone in Engineering was facing similar deadlines and pressures, so there were no distractions. Moreover, coffee and snacks were available in the same room, and a reasonably priced restaurant was also nearby. I could spend a whole day at the University without worrying about food or drink or being disrupted by other students. Resources on the 'VLE' (Blackboard) were accessible on Wi-Fi throughout the building, and if I became stuck lecturers were not far away, and other students were on-hand.

Although most revision in my third year was done at the University, during teaching weeks I was only there during lecture hours, unless I needed to use equipment or software only accessible at the University. Information provided at lectures as notes was also available on 'Blackboard', but there were vital parts or workings which needed to be filled in during lectures.

I had house mates studying business and chemistry, both of whom worked at the general University Library, and it was reported to be a noisy place, in which it was difficult to revise. I found, by contrast, that the Engineering Department in Cardiff had everything one needed, whether it was a computer lab, private conference room, silent library, open-plan multi-purpose room, internet cafe, restaurant or access to lecturers' offices.

University of Leeds

Beth Nunnington (Broadcast Journalism, graduated 2011)

Whilst I was at University I never really thought about the learning spaces, but looking back I think they are important and do make a big difference to students.

The main lecture theatre was in a huge grey building called the 'Roger Stevens Building'. It was uninspiring and old fashioned; during lectures it sometimes became easy to switch off and not pay attention. However in my final year our newsroom and media department were refurbished, which made a massive improvement because the equipment was much better, and we had '24/7' access.

This made study much easier when approaching deadlines because there were fewer people fighting to use the required equipment, which was faster and state of the art.

During our newsroom sessions we each had access to a computer, yet we mainly worked alone in this environment. In seminars we often sat in small discussion groups, but no technology was available. I can see how it would have been effective to use group tables with 'tablet' computers and share visual information, both for research and presentations.

Sitting in the library for many hours became a depressing experience; as most students would testify. It lacked creative space, and at times was incredibly noisy. During busy periods I would often have to wait for a computer to become available, yet I was reluctant to bring in my own laptop, as there was also competition for plug sockets! While I did manage to complete some work in the library, I usually returned to my accommodation because I felt more comfortable there.

Overall I had a great experience at the University of Leeds and the equipment provided specifically for journalism was excellent. Shared resources with other faculties, such as the library, lecture theatres and seminar rooms, would definitely have been improved by better technology.

Beth Nunnington – PR and Social Media Executive

Loughborough University

Verity James   (Information Management and Business Studies, graduated 2013)

During my four-year degree course we were required to complete several pieces of project coursework, which entailed being assigned to groups of six people. As all students in the group would receive the same grade for the quality of the work, it was important that everyone contributed. My first group comprised strongly motivated students who worked well together and contributed; we therefore achieved a very good grade. But I was less lucky in my next group; motivation between students varied, and one student refused to contribute.

I discussed my concerns about this with the tutor and team, as poor commitment would reduce the marks for the whole group. I was told this would be a learning experience for the future. In any company there could be people in your team who do not contribute. Rather than isolate them, the best thing is provide encouragement.

I then visited the non-contributing student to clarify the marks system, explaining that everyone had a lot to offer the group and that we can learn from each other when collaborating. I also explained that the marks for each team member would be based on total effort, and that bringing our knowledge together during self-arranged meetings would benefit everyone. It proved a successful way to obtain participation. Attendance and contributions by team members seemed stronger when a lecturer was present.

I have now discovered from the experience of employment that collaboration in projects at university does transfer to the workplace; and while studying for a professional sales qualification I also learnt that most effective work occurs when people collaborate in groups of four. It is useful to have a dedicated area and display so that team members can share expertise, thereby increasing the group's efficiency and knowledge.

Returning to my university learning, around 75 per cent of timetabled work time was spent in lectures and 25 per cent on group project work. The space available for group work had limited numbers of tables and computer screens, so group study mostly took place in the departmental computer laboratories, which was less efficient. The quality of any teaching space is extremely important. Areas that enable students to collaborate closely in small groups, by sharing examples and experiences, contribute greatly to student learning.

Loughborough University

Tom Peberdy (Banking, Finance and Management, graduated 2013)

At Loughborough the first active learning spaces for groups were installed while I was working in London for my placement year. So I was only used them in my final year. As far as I was aware, group tables were available at only two places on campus. Both sets were available on a first-come, first-served basis.

The tables proved to be very popular. If you wanted to obtain use of a table you had to arrive early or late, and even then tables were often taken. A booking system would have helped, especially if you were planning to work with others on a project.

It was also frustrating sometimes to find that tables were busy but associated screens were unused, when we wanted mainly to use the latter. Screens were invaluable for group coursework as we could show a master document on the screen and work with our laptops to find additional information.

The learning spaces had two drawbacks. There were usually insufficient plug sockets for everyone in a group to charge laptops simultaneously, and laptops had to be plugged in and unplugged to share information with everyone. Wireless equipment would have enabled everyone to connect to the screen and fast interaction between individuals. But better equipment would have generated greater demand for the facilities.

My lectures and tutorials did not involve use of group study tables. But I can see their potential the teaching of certain subjects. The value of such rooms would also vary according to year group. First-year students are typically shy and disinclined to work hard. Group areas would have been especially valuable in the final year, following the experience of working in a collaborative business environment during the placement year. We would have achieved much more from our projects.

University of Manchester

Thomas Beardmore, (Philosophy [BA], International Development and the Environment [MA], graduated 2011 [MA 2012])

During timetabled hours, lectures and lessons were primarily teacher-focused. Lectures were based around slides and visualisers projected onto a large screen. Tutorials were similar, but held with smaller numbers in less formal settings in which discussion was encouraged. Sometimes during tutorials we would split into groups to collaborate on team-based projects. I learnt the most from tutorials, which enabled me to discuss my own work and ideas and talk through queries or theories with the rest of the class.

Outside formal timetabled hours, the course required personal study for the majority of my time - writing essays, researching books and papers, and preparing for tutorials. As this was best undertaken on campus away from home distractions, it was most important that the study spaces were of a high standard. I spent around 75 per cent of personal study time on campus.

For non-ICT work, space was provided primarily in the library, which offered plenty of desk space and plug facilities for laptops. Online resources were easy to access, and there was a good working atmosphere and friends usually to hand for discussions. There were also plenty of quiet ICT suites around the campus which provided easy access to university software and online resources. My 15,000 word master's thesis was written in such a suite – thanks to '24/7' access.

Spaces were also provided for group work, but these were usually defined as areas in which people could make noise. The two group areas I used were simply clusters of tables where groups could sit around, with plug sockets provided nearby for powering laptops etc. They were effective for group discussion but it was sometimes difficult to share visual information among a group as normally we would all be facing inwards. There were two meeting rooms in the library in which groups could use a bigger screen to prepare group PowerPoints etc., but they were often fully booked. Wi-Fi was readily available in all campus buildings, making it easy to use portable devices for group and solo work.

University of Sheffield

Chris Grindley (Politics, graduated 2012)

'Shared Learning Spaces' was a concept that was barely pushed in my three years at Sheffield. Yes, we had a couple of group assignments each year; but no one recommended where the work should be undertaken. The usual solution was to occupy an empty seminar room or a nearby café, preferably somewhere with Wi-Fi.

Our main university library, the 'Information Commons' (IC), did include rooms containing a table for up to eight people. Some also had a large wall-mounted screen into which a laptop could be plugged. But whenever you needed one of these rooms, they were almost always already booked. During my three years, I only managed to obtain a room once. Across the six floors there were several large tables on which you could work, though these were often also occupied. They were also too large for holding discussions.

Politics is a subject that requires discussion and debate. But my course contained only three 50-minute seminars and three 50-minute lectures a week. So in all, only two and a half hours were provided each week for structured discussion on political and philosophical subjects led by a professor or lecturer.

Small-group projects suitable for undertaking in a 'Shared Learning Space' would have been preferable to seemingly endless solitary reading. Obviously each person has a different approach to learning, and many students are happy to sit in silence, read and make notes.

Sadly, politics at Sheffield was mostly concerned with individual rather than shared learning.

University of Worcester

Max Young (PE and Sports Studies, graduated 2012)

During my course most teaching time was divided between lectures delivered to 100 – 200 students, and seminars, which were provided for groups of 20 – 30 students but delivered in lecture style. There was little provision for group study.

Only occasionally was a seminar task set that was appropriate for a small group, typically three or four students.

Most working spaces available on campus were intended for individual study. There was only one small area suitable for groups which had access to a computer with a group screen. Computers were available in the 'Resource Centre', but it was usually too busy, especially during assessment time. As it was difficult to find a place for group work on campus, group tasks such as presentations were usually divided up and worked on individually. Lack of group space also made it difficult to rehearse presentations. The only group study zone on campus could not be pre-booked.

Provision for individual study, on the other hand, was usually excellent though during busy periods the capacity was insufficient. When studying alone I preferred to be on campus with its access to resources, but during busy periods I studied at home knowing that much time could otherwise be wasted in trying to find a free computer.

At times lectures seemed pointless because lecturers simply read from slides with little additional input. Because these were afterwards placed on the 'VLE', the information could have been accessed from home.

Seminars involved more interaction between students, but they mostly took place in rooms designed for front-of-class instruction, and were therefore unsuitable for small-group interactions. I am sure that the teaching would have been more interesting if teaching spaces had been more suitable.

Lectures to large numbers of students sometimes do not provide a good understanding of a topic. Greater interaction in spaces designed for group discussion and study would have provided a greater understanding of module content.

PART 7

Sponsors

Crestron

Founded in 1968, Crestron has established itself as a leading supplier of control and automation systems for education, business, homes, hospitals, hotels and other locations. Integration is the essence of its business. Crestron combines 'intelligent' control systems that traditionally would have existed separately; AV, IT, building management, and comfort (heating, lighting). Delivering full capabilities from a single source helps to maximize the return on investment in facilities, and offers the potential for increasing scalability as needs change.

To ensure that Crestron's capabilities remain at the forefront of technological developments, it partners with the world's leading technology giants, including Microsoft, Apple, Cisco and Intel.

Crestron contributes to education by making the control of technology for teaching spaces as engaging and intuitive as possible, enabling educators to enhance their teaching. It seeks to provide reliable technology so that users can integrate technology in their work without difficulty. Behind the scenes, so to speak, Crestron systems can automatically monitor environments, giving support teams crucial information and the ability to manage their estate effectively.

Many of the world's leading universities have become Crestron Connected™ campuses, and enjoy the benefits of Crestron's hardware and infrastructure in teaching and estate management.

Crestron Case Study

Crestron Powers New Surgical Teaching at Trinity College, Dublin

Trinity College's Bioscience Centre, which costing €131 million, includes a state-of-the-art anatomy dissection theatre comprising 13 workstations that replicate a full operating-theatre experience for students. Each workstation supports a mix of audio and visual sources which are integrated via Crestron control processors. The system integrator for the facility, Jones AV Ltd, was a finalist in the 2013 EMEA InAVation Awards.

Each workstation is a replica of an operational theatre and provides students with a realistic reconstruction of what they will find in their professional life. 'We have tried to recreate an operating theatre environment so the students would get used to the real deal,' commented Jones AV Director, Ingo Aicher, adding: 'The only noticeable difference here is that in a hospital's operating rooms the doctors are in charge of the system, while at the Dublin facility at Trinity, we have provided lecturers with "super-user functionality" and override rights.'

Crestron Star Network

The workstations consist of an operating table for donor bodies surrounded by an array of technical wizardry: ceiling mounted theatre lights, a 42" monitor, HD monitor and corresponding camera, medical-grade video capture PC, ceiling-mounted speakers and microphones, which are controlled via a Crestron touch screen linked to a local Crestron processor.

Back in the equipment rack, each of 13 local CP2E processors relays data to the heart of a star network, an AV2 control system that combines with the video hub, media matrix, VC kit and scalers. Although there are some independent items, at the stations the control of most equipment (lights, displays, capture PC, mics etc.) is unified through a Crestron touch screen and two further iPads which include the super-user functions. 'We chose Crestron as a control system for its reliability and flexibility', says Ingo Aicher. 'The options a Crestron system provides allowed us to accommodate any integration wishes of the client, while knowing that we can 100 per cent rely on its functionality, uptime and customer support.'

Students can connect to the lecturers' workstation via the touch screen and use their live video feeds to ask questions. Lecturers can engage in private dialogue or send content to several workstations for a multi-point conference. Lecturers can also override students at their workstations and route images and video to other monitors. Videoconferencing equipment also provides for remote teaching.

Custom GUI Design

In operating-theatre environments it is crucial to have the right function at your fingertips. And more than likely this fingertip will be covered by a latex glove. This reduces the ability of an operator to be exact with touch and thus larger touch-screen buttons are required although physical space remains tight. 'In order to deliver a system which has plenty of input/output control functions, we could not simply deliver a control system where we cram a lot of buttons onto a single page', commented Ingo Aicher. 'Therefore, we developed a drill down style menu, which people are familiar with since the dawn of the iPod, and fine-tuned it to integrate a combination of hard-button features with function page drill down. The system delivers source to destination or any desired page within three touches of a button.'

Positive Prognosis

In producing a reconstruction of working operating-theatre spaces, as much attention had to be paid to the AV/IT kit and networking as to the physical construction of the room. The installation at Trinity College shows how a Crestron control solution can provide unparalleled scope for customisation. It allowed the team at Jones AV Ltd to tailor the facility to the college's specific needs. Dr Paul Tierney, Head of Anatomy at Trinity College, Dublin, has observed:

'We have really benefitted from the AV installation. The courses have gained momentum, simply through students being more motivated to study and eager to come in and use the facility. The Department has managed to secure high profile external bookings for the facility for surgical training courses and international conventions, which simply would have passed us by if we did not have this unique facility to offer. The amazing positive feedback we get from visiting professionals is not only confirmation of our vision, but testament to Jones AV sharing that vision and translating it into a truly great and easy to use system.'

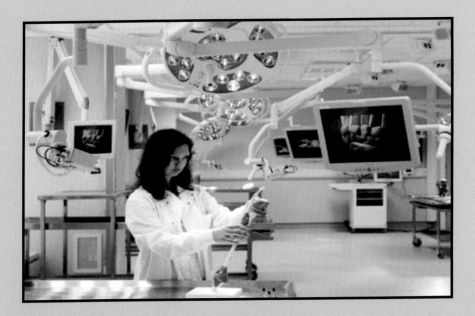

Anatomy Dissection Theatre
Trinity College Dublin

NEC Display Solutions

NEC benefits from over a hundred years of company expertise in technological innovation to deliver outstanding visual display equipment for individuals, organisations and society. With its own Research and Development division, NEC is one of the world's leading manufacturers, offering the widest product range in the market.

It produces both projectors and displays for all requirements, from portable devices through to systems for business, together with technically advanced displays for more demanding facilities, such as command and control rooms, multiscreen cinemas, and lecture theatres with multiple displays. Through its Solution Partner Network, NEC provides technology solutions to complement its product portfolio.

In the education environment NEC offers touch-enabled displays and collaborative DisplayNote software, tools widely used to increase student participation and encourage active learning. NEC's projectors and large-format displays have long been standard equipment in universities, but at some leading universities such as Warwick, the student AV experience has now expanded outdoors with the installation of an LED video wall in the university's central piazza. The NEC 17.5m2 outdoor screen will show live streams of ceremonies, international sporting events, digital arts and student films, enhancing the reputation of Warwick University as a centre for innovation in teaching and research, and with world-class links to manufacturing and business.

As active learning relies on the sharing of visual information, the quality of image and technological functionality are set to become even more important in education. NEC is the perfect partner for the design and installation of display technology for active learning spaces.

NEC Display Solutions Case Study
Düsseldorf Students Evaluate the Use of Technology in Lectures

More Fun and Success in Learning

In lectures at colleges and universities, there is now an even greater need for improvement in the use of innovative presentation techniques. This is the conclusion of a project study in the Industrial Engineering degree programme at the University of Applied Sciences in Düsseldorf. Eight students interviewed fellow students and lecturers extensively on the use of modern presentation techniques in lectures. The project was supported by NEC Display Solutions. The company supports a variety of research and education projects in order to allow evaluation of innovative teaching methods.

In the process they evaluated in particular, possibilities using the DisplayNote solution which would make individual seminars and lectures more engaging and purposeful. Multiple devices can use a WLAN router connected to the lecturer's PC with DisplayNote: Tablets, PCs, Notebooks and smartphones can be networked. This works perfectly across platforms and saves educational institutions the costs of expensive new acquisitions of the commitment to a single vendor.

With DisplayNote the same software runs on all devices with a single user interface, this whiteboard-like software is thus available to every student. Using this they can link to the lecturer's teaching notes on the Tablet, add their own notes, and save them. All marking and labelling methods which are offered by traditional whiteboards or PDF editing programmes can also be found here. Because these tools are only virtual slides of the material presented, it does not matter what output format they have. Consequently  lecturers have the freedom to choose whether they should rely on their own PowerPoint files, a blank document as a Tablet replacement or special learning software. Therefore they do not need to rework their digital teaching materials, but can reuse existing material. Through the use of an integrated message function, messages can be sent directly to individuals or to groups of students. Furthermore, the projector can be fully controlled by the NEC Edition, allowing lecturers full control to freeze images or change the input for example, even without the remote control.

In the unanimous opinion of the students, the annotation function has a particularly significant value. This allows the students to record their thoughts immediately without having to wait until lecturers have their materials ready to download on the university server. This advantage in terms of time has a very positive impact.

Even the simple collaborative exercises performed by the students proved positive, in particular, the respondents liked the easy exchange of working materials. The possible collaboration on group-specific or individual tasks or the presentation of results from a group project without interruptions caused by media or equipment proved to be especially helpful in practical tests. Respondents unanimously praised the ease of opportunity to exchange ideas in a straightforward manner and to share and discuss results within the group. "Students, especially in the first terms of their studies, prefer to work in groups. In their everyday life at the university they feel more comfortable in groups, and value the exchanges with other students", says Karin Ziegler, research associate of the University of Applied Sciences in Düsseldorf.

Overall, the students want a less traditional teaching approach, the methodology used by the likes of DisplayNote suits them better. In practical applications it turned out that the subject matter was much better understood and it was easier for the students to keep in mind what they had seen and heard.

The students also still appreciate, projection on a large screen. Many respondents indicated that it was important to be able to follow the gestures of the professor. The combination of an intelligent whiteboard and a modern Tablet solution thus appears to provide the best experience.

Since the majority of students already own a Tablet or a laptop, there are scarcely any practical limits set in the use of innovative solutions for teaching activities. 'Students now use very different devices for the communication and technical needs of life. The fact that these cannot be integrated into their principal occupation, namely studying at the university, is an exasperating anachronism for many of them', Professor Kati Schmengler of the University of Applied Sciences in Düsseldorf reports. 'DisplayNote can now make them much happier and offer greater opportunities for learning'.

Revolabs

Revolabs is a premier provider of audio systems and equipment for a wide range of markets including higher education. Voice amplification in lecture theatres and large active learning spaces is essential for modern learning. Learning capture systems increasingly provide material for students to re-visit through an institution's VLE – (virtual learning environment). Lecture rooms and active learning spaces are being designed to encourage teachers to move around because a stationary position behind a podium makes it difficult to engage and motivate students.

Combining the ultimate in flexibility with sleek stylish products, Revolabs' wireless microphones facilitate natural mobility by allowing participants to move about a teaching or work space unhindered by wires and be heard. Digital audio quality allows students to 'hear every word' while teachers speak with their normal voice.

Revolabs wireless microphone systems use a government-reserved frequency band outside the UHF/VHF RF bands that have undergone frequency reallocations and not within the ever more crowded 2.4 GHz band used for Wi-Fi and Bluetooth applications in corporate environments. They are digitally secure (encrypted), environmentally friendly (rechargeable), and immune from buzzing interference from mobile phone signals.

Revolabs wireless microphones are robust, intuitive solutions for a wide variety of higher education needs.

Revolabs Case Study

Higher Education Demands Higher Audio Quality

Revolabs' Executive HD™ Wireless Microphone Systems Right at Home in University of Surrey's Renovated Lecture Hall

Overview

Located in the south of England, the University of Surrey is an international university with a worldwide reputation for excellence in teaching and research. In August 2011, the university broke ground on the renovation of its flagship lecture hall, which seats more than 300 people and is used heavily for a variety of educational, conference, and broadcasting events. The project included a new ceiling for the theatre, major work to the front wall, and a new AV infrastructure featuring a high-end wireless microphone system.

Challenge

"The microphone system is a key component of this installation," said Simon Loder, CTS-D IT/AV systems analyst at the University of Surrey. "When selecting a solution, our main requirements were that it be a high-quality, resilient system with rechargeable microphones, remote management capabilities, and immunity to interference caused by other radio mics being used in the area. In addition, as the system would be used day to day by a number of different academics who might be unfamiliar with its operation, ease of use was a high priority." To satisfy these criteria, the University chose Revolabs Executive HD™ 4- and 8-channel wireless microphone systems, in addition to six HD directional tabletop microphones, two HD wearable micro and two HD XLR adaptors for handheld microphones.

Soluiton / Results

The HD 4- and 8-channel units are mounted in a rack and feed Ecler MIMO88 digital audio matrixes and NZA amplifiers. Speakers for the system are recessed behind acoustically transparent cloth in the theatre's front wall, ensuring optimal audio quality while presenting the cleanest possible look. The systems' charging stations are connected to a local PC for management and firmware updates.

'The high-quality 7.1 surround sound that the Revolabs systems offers is outstanding, and the feedback we've received from users is very positive. They find the units easy to use and love the rechargeable functionality. The Executive HD's performance is not generally commented on, which is actually a really good sign. Negative feelings are always expressed openly, but praise isn't.

All and all, the Executive HD has more than met our expectations."

Benefits

- Simple to operate
- Variety of microphone options available
- Exceptional audio quality with immunity to interference
- Remote management software for monitoring and controlling networked systems
- Rechargeable microphones provide up to eight hours of talk time

TOP-TEC – Technical Furniture Solutions

With a manufacturing history based in the West Midlands since 1957, TOP-TEC has for many years been a leading supplier of lecterns, IT desks, and technology security solutions to UK universities. Although TOP-TEC has the in-house design and manufacturing capability to take a new product from invention to installation, it regularly consults with universities and specialist groups to ensure that education receives fit-for-purpose products. As technology advances, so do the requirements for technical furniture associated with visualisers, control panels, and lecture capture systems.

The activation of expensive equipment, such as lecture capture systems, requires easy access. Control units cannot be hidden behind locked doors. TOP-TEC has developed and patented a shelf that holds systems securely in place while providing access and security through an aperture. TOP-TEC is also ahead of the game in two other areas. When equipped with technology from joint-sponsors Crestron and NEC, its Synergy collaborative table provides instant wired and wireless connection for any mobile device to a group NEC screen. Synergy tables are proving popular as 'BYOD' (Bring Your Own Device) solutions in formal active learning areas and ad-hoc social spaces.

For a more tradition classroom setting, TOP-TEC's 'Versatile Flip-Top Desk' transforms instantly from being a PC-enabled IT desk (with screen, keyboard and mouse connected to a securely mounted PC) in to a simple technology-free desk for different learning scenarios. Universities such as Wolverhampton have substantially increased their room utilisation by using these transformable desks.

TOP-TEC Case Study

UNIVERSITY OF
WOLVERHAMPTON
KNOWLEDGE • INNOVATION • ENTERPRISE

Venus Flip-Top Desks

Using Top-Tec's Venus versatile flip-top desks, this learning room at the University of Wolverhampton is equally effective as an IT suite for 64 undergraduates, or as standard desks for non-IT tuition.

The desks conceal a screen keyboard and mouse, which become instantly available to the student with the pull of small lever beneath the desk surface. The robust steel frames are purposely designed to support heavy computer equipment, and a side-mounted computer cages secure the hardware from casual theft, bumps and knocks.

Transformed from IT Lab to teaching space in seconds..

Inbuilt cable trunking provides neat and easy cable management for power and data cables. If required, adjoining desks can be bolted together to create a more permanent room layout. And when it comes to examinations, the room is equally at home as an IT suite or configured with standard exam desks.

Benefits

Before the installation of Top-Tec's desks, undergraduate Psychology courses at Wolverhampton were previously allocated 3 teaching spaces on a permanent basis. The use of these versatile desks has freed up the other two rooms that have now become centrally bookable, and increased the space utilisation of the building at a time when, for the next two years as Wolverhampton constructs two new buildings, space is at a particular premium.

TOP-TEC design and manufacture a range of technical furniture solutions that combine people and technology, helping educational organisations to achieve the best possible outcomes from Learning and Teaching spaces.

Manufactured in Birmingham, Top-Tec's Venus versatile desks are available in a range of sizes and colours to match any room. To better support disabled students, there is also an electronically operated height adjustable version too.

Interactive Table – by TOP-TEC

Interactive tables are not new in the market, but they are growing in popularity because of the way that they allow users to interact naturally with visual information and collaboratively with each other. There's a good reason why interactive whiteboards haven't become popular in higher education or corporate environments. They can be good for teacher-led instruction and presentations - when a single person is leading the group - but as adults, congregating around a wall-mounted board working together on something that needs our considered intellectual input, the experience just doesn't feel right; it conflicts with our human instinct. Collaborative learning requires students to work together as a single team and bring all their individual experiences and expertise into play, and TOP-TEC's interactive table perfectly provides this natural-feeling environment.

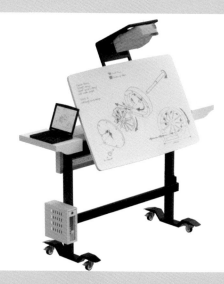

Sitting or standing around a TOP-TEC interactive table helps teams to advance their interaction; it's a much more natural environment for working together manipulating visual information to problem-solve or investigate complex scenarios. And easily relocated through standard doorways without having to remove any equipment, TOP-TECs robust intelligent design provides organisations with a mobile resource that can be shared between rooms and departments, and delivering a great return on investment. The height and angle of the table are effortlessly adjusted by electric motors, quickly creating the perfect interface to advance team-dynamics through a natural collaborative experience.

New for 2014, TOP-TEC's interactive table incorporates the latest finger-touch interactive projectors from Epson. Switch-on the securely-housed computer or connect a laptop and the interactive functions work immediately with your Windows software; no new apps to learn – instant productivity.

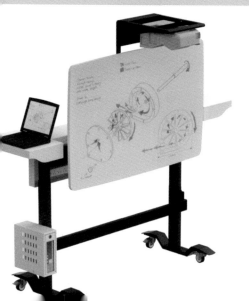

WolfVision

Founded in 1966, WolfVision is a successful family-owned Austrian company involved in the AV (audio visual) industry. Since the 1990s it has concentrated on the design and manufacture of sophisticated visualisers – also known as 'document cameras'. It invests annually 15 per cent of its turnover in research and development. It offers a comprehensive range of both desktop and ceiling-mounted visualisers.

The company has regional offices in the UK, USA, Canada, UAE, Singapore and Japan, ensuring global coverage for its growing customer base. In 2008 WolfVision moved into a new, purpose-built, award-winning, environmentally friendly headquarters building in Klaus, Austria.

WolfVision products enable photos, documents and objects to be digitised, magnified and displayed 'live' on-screen. This encourages participation and interaction by audiences, and enables learning spaces to be effectively utilised. Being able to see material displayed in outstanding detail, including '3D', helps students to understand concepts and provides the opportunity to add real-life examples to theoretical teaching.

Many of today's standards in visualiser technology were developed and introduced by WolfVision, which is justly regarded as a pioneer of the visualiser industry. But its continuing prominence is based on its undoubted contribution to the improvement of learning and its ability to stay at the forefront of development.

TOP-TEC Lectern for WolfVision VZ-3s Visualiser

Flip charts are large, dry-erase boards bigger still, and writing areas under visualisers comparatively small; that was until now.

Flip charts and dry-erase boards force you to turn your back on your audience when you want to use them, whereas visualisers are used facing forward from behind the desk or lectern, enabling lecturers to maintain eye-contact and the engagement of their students. This book covers in some detail the many advantages of using visualisers; all of which still apply here.

In collaboration with WolfVision, TOP-TEC has purposely designed a new lectern so that a WolfVision VZ-3s visualiser provides a capture area the size of a large A2 piece of paper (594mm x 420mm). Objects can still be placed under the visualiser, but now when a lecturer wants to make additional notes or explain a concept visually, he or she has a large area to work with. They now have the additional benefit of space to show an object and annotate around it.

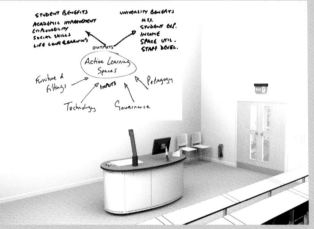

WolfVision's V-Connect Software allows the information to be captured, or even viewed on mobile devices in the learning space, making the solution appropriate for a range of teaching spaces and learning scenarios.

As can be seen in the diagrams above, as the lecturer is writing and engaging with students, they have a large image to see, instead of struggling to see small text on a flip chart or dry-erase board.

TOP-TEC's engineering allows WolfVision's VZ-3s to be used in this way with a wide range of its Voyager lecterns.

PART 8
Acknowledgements

This book has been produced thanks to financial support from sponsors who shared my vision to publicise active learning and related technology to influential figures at UK Universities. The book includes an introduction to each sponsoring company, together with information about its capabilities and examples of installations to which it has contributed. Special thanks are owed to **Clive Beardmore**, Managing Director of TOP-TEC, who provided time for completion of this project.

All of the sponsors recognise that other companies also provide technical resources for learning and teaching environments. It is to the sponsors' credit that they have not sought to influence this work.

In addition to Clive Beardmore, I wish to thank **Matthew Browning** at Crestron, **Neil Hartigan** at NEC, **Mary Mathis** at Revolabs and especially **Thomas Zangerle** at WolfVision for their support. I am grateful to ALL the contributors who have extended the scope of my original conception by expanding the discussion of complex issues around learning spaces. The contributors include academics, policy-makers, learning spaces specialists, audio visual integrators and students. Their writings amount to a rich tapestry of experiences.

In addition to the real editor **Robert Peberdy** – whose expertise has greatly enhanced this book - and the designer **Neil Duffy**, I would like to thank the following for their contributions and other influences that inspired me to make this book happen.

Simon Birkett (Technology Enhanced Learning Manager, University of Derby)
Nicholas Burwell (Architect, Burwell Deakins, London)
Professor Charles Crook (Director, Learning Sciences Research Institute, University of Nottingham)
Matthew Green (Assistant Director, Academic and Learning Support, University of Wolverhampton)
Rob Hyde (Service Manager, Audio Visual, University of Bath)
James Pearson-Jenkins (Senior Lecturer, University of Wolverhampton)
Cathy Rex (Director of Library Services, University of the West of England)
Nigel Thomas (Learning Spaces Design and Development Manager, Aberystwyth University)
Sam Williams (Space Planning and Strategy Manager, University of Lincoln)
And I am also grateful to the recent graduates who provided accounts of their experiences at their respective universities.

Finally, to my long suffering wife **Elaine**, thank you for your continuing support. One day I will make a difference!

About the Author

Duncan was born in Loughborough where the local grammar school tried its best to educate him and instead instilled a life-long love of sport. After leaving college Duncan was briefly employed as a professional tennis coach before joining the junior ranks of the Foreign and Commonwealth Office (FCO). Duncan initially spent three enjoyable years in London before heading to Germany to work at the British Consulate in Munich for two years. Having resigned from the FCO, Duncan remained in Germany working at the American Embassy in Bonn before returning to the UK in 1988 as a married man.

Since 1988 Duncan has been employed in the world of technology and audio visual sales. Temporarily distracted by gaining a Certificate in Education, it was writing about computers that got Duncan his first words commercially published, including dozens of articles for titles such as Indie, ComputerActive and PC Advisor magazines.
In 2001 Duncan took a career break to write full time, and in 2003 his first novel – 'Out of Control' – was published in hardback.

In 2009, Duncan successfully pitched and jointly authored 'Brilliant Meetings' for Pearson Education. Brilliant Meetings has subsequently been translated into French, Italian, Arabic and Chinese. Digital publishing opened new opportunities, and in 2010 Duncan self-published 'Communicate, Collaborate, Educate - Using PowerPoint' as a Kindle e-book. In early 2012, 'Out of Control' was updated and published as a Kindle e-book under the new name of 'Youthenasia'.

More recently, Duncan has immersed himself in all aspects of collaboration, understanding the needs of both the corporate world and higher education. Too often organisations focus on a narrow aspect of collaboration - usually technology - without recognising and understanding the total requirements for successful implementations.

Since early 2013, Duncan has worked for Dalen Ltd (TOP-TEC), and enjoys the opportunity to develop new technical furniture solutions and clearly show clients how these are integral to their collaborative aspirations

Together with his wife Elaine, Duncan lives in Droitwich, and they are both very proud of their two grown-up children independently forging their own successful careers.

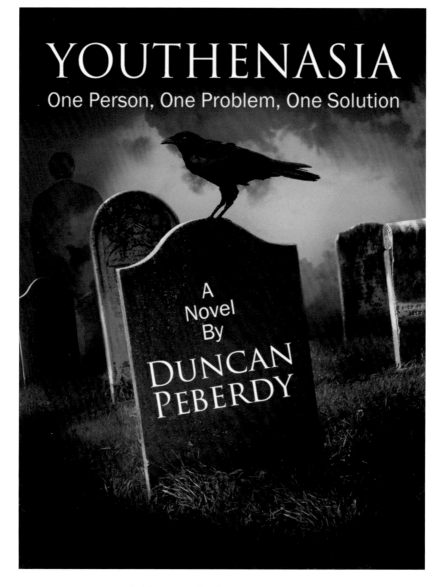

Available in Kindle format from Amazon
for Kindle, iPad, Android, PC & Mac

Also by Duncan Peberdy

Youthenasia – a novel.

Available from Amazon for a ridiculously low price!

On a cold October night, shortly after tottering away in high heels from the Barley Mow pub, Debbie Green is abducted. The fifteen year old's poisoned body is discovered early the following morning in the undergrowth of a rural lane. Her seemingly motiveless death mystifies even the police.

Two weeks later, underneath the railway bridge where he had been spraying a graffiti mural, the still-warm body of Jonathan Braidwood is stumbled upon by an elderly couple. His wrists are bound, neck bruised, and the same home made concoction circulated through his veins.

More teenage murders followed; dysfunctional petty criminals with long lists of anti-social misdemeanours and banning orders. And with the eradication of such troublesome yobs, the outrage that greeted the first two seemingly innocent deaths subsides. Teenagers are in fear of their lives. Pensioners have reclaimed their town centre and for all but the youth, life in Droitwich improves by the day.

One month after the killings commenced, Detective Inspector Jim Jarvis and his incident team at West Mercia Police remain baffled. Baffled by the motive, baffled by the identity of the perpetrator. The time has come for Professor Martin Noakes from Birmingham's Regional Forensic Psychology Service to build up a psychological profile of the killer. Would his expertise help to uncover the murderer's identity? And how many teenagers have still to die before a personal revenge is satisfied?

With the hither-too sleepy town of Droitwich Spa at its core, Youthenasia poses questions about morality on a journey that connects Cornwall, the Lake District and Munich into the landscapes.

Youthenasia: The permanent eradication of troublesome teenagers.

How good are YOUR detective skills?

Youthenasia is also the **ultimate 1980's Pop-Music Quiz**; expertly crafted into the text are the titles to 85 Top 20 UK single hits from the 1980s.* Song's by top-selling artists such as: George Michael, Duran Duran, Tears for Fears, Depeche Mode, Iron Maiden, Michael Jackson, Bruce Springsteen, David Bowie and many more.

85 song titles for you to detect. The trouble is, you'll be so engrossed in this page-turner that you'll be a clueless as West Mercia Police.

*As listed in the Guinness book 'Hits of the 80s'